EASY READING
SHAKESPEARE
VOLUME ONE

By the same author:

Easy Reading Shakespeare Volume Two: The Bard in Bite-Size Verse, The Book Guild, 2006

Easy Reading Shakespeare Volume Three: The Bard in Bite-Size Verse, The Book Guild, 2006

Kenneth Grahame's The Wind in the Willows in Bite-Size Verse, The Book Guild, 2005

EASY READING
SHAKESPEARE
VOLUME ONE

The Bard in Bite-Size Verse

Richard Cuddington

Book Guild Publishing
Sussex, England

First published in Great Britain in 2005 by
The Book Guild Ltd
Pavilion View
19 New Road
Brighton
BN1 1UF

Typesetting in Times by
Keyboard Services, Luton, Bedfordshire

Printed in Great Britain by
Antony Rowe Ltd, Chippenham, Wiltshire

A catalogue record for this book is available from
The British Library

ISBN 978 1 84624 151 2

To Julia

CONTENTS

FOREWORD

I feel passionately about Shakespeare. His work is truly one of the great gifts that all English speakers inherit as part of their birthright. This is why I am delighted to write the foreword to this volume, which whilst simplifying ten major plays into modern verse has nevertheless still captured the essence of each of the plays included. For those who are daunted by the original language of Shakespeare, this book is a wonderfully entertaining and easy introduction to the plots and major characters of some of Shakespeare's best-loved plays.

These adaptations will appeal to young and old alike and I hope they will encourage readers to experience the actual plays through the excellent theatre productions, film and audio recordings that abound today.

Richard Briers

'I want Antonio's flesh
I will have my bond,' said he

THE MERCHANT OF VENICE

Antonio – a merchant
Lived in Venice town of old,
He was a wheeler-dealer,
A guy who bought and sold.

He was known both far and wide
For kindness without end
As he'd shell out hard earned cash
To help a needy friend.

He wouldn't ask for interest,
He wouldn't charge a fee,
He'd hand the money over,
They'd get the loan for free.

These gestures went down well
With everyone he knew,
Except tight-fisted Shylock,
A moneylender too.

Shylock objected strongly
Through all his ancient bones
Because he made great profit
Charging interest on loans.

Antonio thought him mean
And, fond of playing games,
When he bumped into Shylock,
He'd often call him names.

Shylock bore this with patience,
He just let him have his say,
But beneath his breath he vowed:
'I'll be revenged some day.'

Bassanio – a noble,
Was Antonio's best friend.
But though of noble blood
He had little cash to spend.

He'd spend what cash he had
As men of rank will do,
And when his funds ran short
Antonio helped him through.

One day Bassanio said,
'Antonio, I'm bewitched,
By this really gorgeous girl
And I'm hoping to get hitched.'

He said, 'I love her dearly,
She really is a honey;
What makes it even better,
She's got pots and pots of money.

'If she'll become my bride
I'll be such a lucky bloke,
With money and a wife I'll solve
Two problems at a stroke.

'But I need cash to aid my bid,'
He went on to say.
'I need three thousand ducats – and
I need it right away.'

Now at that time Antonio
Didn't have the cash in hand
So said he'd ask old Shylock
To lend him the three grand.

He wasn't very worried
As he had some ships at sea,
Due in Venice by next month
With silk, spices, gold and tea.

So they went to visit Shylock
To seek a three grand loan.
Shylock muttered, 'Disrespect
Is all this man has shown.

'He insults me all the time,
He berates the things I do,
He calls me misbeliever,
Cut throat dog – and lazy too.

'He hates me earning interest
Though my margins are quite slim,
I will be cursed, there is no doubt
If I give help to him.'

Antonio lost patience.
'Shylock, speak to me,' says he,
'Answer me right now,
Will you lend the cash to me?'

Shylock thought before responding
In a quiet, angry way,
'You want my cash, yet did you not
Spit at me yesterday.

'You call me dog but has a dog
Got any cash to spend?
I think this most unlikely,
Let alone three grand to lend.

'And you expect me also
To let your insults go.'
Antonio said, 'Then lend it
As if lending to a foe.'

'Oh how you storm!' old Shylock cried.
'Won't you be friends with me?
To prove my generosity
You can have the loan for free.'

Antonio was astounded,
For the offer was most kind,
It was without a trace of doubt
The best deal he would find.

'But,' Shylock said, beginning
To weave a devilish mesh,
'If not repaid by due date
You lose a pound of flesh.'

Antonio cried, 'Agreed,
I'll gladly sign the bond.'
Bassanio said he was convinced
Antonio had been conned.

He said it was a bad deal
Antonio had just bought,
But Shylock smiled and murmured that
The deal was, 'only sport.'

Antonio signed the bond and said,
'My ships will soon arrive.
Old Shylock will not get his flesh.
You'll see – I will survive.'

The girl Bassanio loved
And was set to woo and win,
Lived with her trusted servants,
Having lost her nearest kin.

She owned a vast estate,
She was a wealthy dame,
And Portia of Belmont
Was this good lady's name.

She was a real good looker,
Very nice – and clever too.
Suitors came from far and wide –
They sometimes had to queue.

Her father knew a lot of men
Would want her for their bride,
So he devised a clever plan
Some months before he died.

A most ingenious scheme it was,
For he'd had a wily touch,
To find a really worthy groom
For the child he loved so much.

His plan was like a lottery:
Three riddles to be read,
Each carved upon a casket
Made of silver, gold and lead.

Who found the proper meaning,
Though the meaning tried to hide,
Would win the hand of Portia
And take her for his bride.

Many tried their luck and failed
And sadly went their way,
Portia was delighted
But of course she didn't say.

Her thoughts were of Bassanio
Whom she'd met some years before,
So her heart beat very fast
When he knocked at Belmont's door.

He went into the casket room,
Wild thoughts raced through his head,
But concentrating hard he chose
The one made out of lead.

It was the very hardest choice
He'd made in all his life,
But it was the one to win
Sweet Portia for his wife.

Then Bassanio confessed
He'd been a two faced lad,
For noble birth and ancestry
Were really all he had.

Portia was very gracious,
She said she didn't mind,
For despite his lack of money
She thought him quite a find.

She said that all she had was his,
And then one special thing
She gave him most affectionately –
A lovely, jewelled ring.

Bassanio said, 'Thank you.'
A grave look on his brow,
He put it on his finger
And made this solemn vow.

'I'll wear this ring forever,
Not let it from my sight,
It will stay here on my finger
Every morning, noon and night.'

They began their plans to wed,
There seemed no time to lose,
But then a messenger arrived
And he brought fearful news.

He had hastened from Antonio,
The news was bad indeed;
Bassanio turned ghostly white
As the others watched him read.

'Sweet Portia, gentle lady,'
Bassanio softly said,
'These sad and dreadful words
Are the worst I've ever read.

'When I first professed my love
I told you I had no wealth,
That all I had was my good name
And, of course, abundant health.

'But I should have truly told you
That my funds were really small,
In fact I should have stated
That there were no funds at all.

'Antonio lent me money
To win you for my wife,
And now it seems this favour
Will cost my friend his life.'

He read Antonio's note,
'Dear Bassanio,' it said,
'All my ships are lost at sea:
This means I'll soon be dead.

'I owe my bond to Shylock,
It's what I now must give,
And when he's cut his pound of flesh
How can I hope to live?'

And then he asked Bassanio
To visit ere he died,
'Oh go at once and take some gold!'
Fair Portia quickly cried.

'Let Shylock have ten times his bond
To save your dear friend's head,
But first of all I must insist
The two of us be wed.

'For then my money will be yours,
I'll be your legal wife,
And then you can depart with haste
To save Antonio's life.'

Once wed Bassanio hurried off,
He went to save his friend,
But when he got to Venice found
That Shylock would not bend.

The date the loan was due
Had been past for quite a while,
And Shylock claimed his bond in full –
Insisting on a trial.

And so a day had now been fixed,
This strange case would be heard,
Before the Duke of Venice who
Would have the final word.

When Bassanio left for Venice
His wife seemed calm to him
But Portia thought that Shylock's threat
Was not an idle whim.

She feared the worst would happen,
That Shylock would win the day,
She wondered how she could assist –
Then she worked out a way.

She had a distant cousin,
A lawyer by his trade;
She thought, 'He'll shield Antonio
From Shylock's vicious blade.'

And sure enough, he sent her robes
And notes how to proceed,
That she might win the case in court
And get Antonio freed.

Portia and her maid got dressed
In the robes they had been lent,
And then set off for Venice town
Armed with the notes he'd sent.

The Duke declared that she could plead
Antonio's case in court,
He didn't rate her chances much
But didn't voice this thought.

And so Antonio's trial began.
Portia's disguise was good,
So no-one recognised her
In her lawyer's cape and hood.

'Shylock' she said, 'the law is clear,
There is no controversy,
Your bond is yours by right to have
But can you not show mercy?'

Portia spoke of mercy,
How it was doubly blessed,
To those who gave and who received
But, as everyone there guessed,

Shylock would not change his mind,
He claimed his bond in full,
Insisting on his pound of flesh –
Her fine words had no pull.

Bassanio then offered
The three grand – even more –
But Shylock simply shook his head
And cried, 'Apply the law!'

Portia said the law must stand
As laid down in the books,
'Oh wise young judge!' old Shylock cried,
'You're older than your looks.'

Portia asked to see the bond.
Perusing it she said,
'Shylock is due his pound of flesh,
From everything I've read.'

She turned to Shylock pleading,
'Show mercy and take the cash.'
Shylock's answer flew right back,
Resolute, in a flash.

'I want Antonio's flesh,
I will have my bond,' said he.
'By my soul I promise you
Fine words can't alter me.'

Everyone in court now feared
For poor Antonio's life,
Portia told him to prepare
And Shylock whet his knife.

Shylock brandished the sharpened blade
In a vicious kind of way;
Portia asked Antonio,
'Have you last words to say?'

Antonio was very calm,
Though close to his last breath,
He said that he'd prepared his mind
To meet untimely death.

He held Bassanio by the hand,
And said 'Don't grieve for me,
Commend me to your dear, sweet wife
Who I shan't live to see.'

Shylock cried, 'We're wasting time,
Give sentence right away,
I want to have my forfeit,
I'll brook no more delay.'

'It shall be so,' Portia replied,
'The forfeit must be paid,
Someone bring a set of scales
To see the flesh is weighed.

'And Shylock when you take it
Take no more than your due,
Just one pound is all the flesh
The law decrees to you.'

'Oh upright judge!' he cried again,
'You're truly very fair.'
He raised his knife and cruelly told
His victim to prepare.

'But stay your hand,' said Portia.
'One word must now be said:
Take care that when you cut the flesh
No drop of blood be shed.'

Shylock stopped dead in his tracks,
Let out an anguished cry,
For he had hoped most fervently
Antonio would die.

He said, 'I'll take the money.'
But she'd have none of it.
She told him he must take the flesh –
Take every little bit.

'But,' she warned, 'take any blood
Or more than the pound laid down,
And by the law you then shall die.'
Shylock began to frown.

'Give me the cash!' he cried aloud,
'And then just let me go.'
'Now wait a moment,' Portia said,
'There's more you need to know.

'You threatened good Antonio
To satisfy your hate,
And therefore your entire wealth
Is forfeit to the state.

'And Shylock there's another thing,
Your life is forfeit too,
You can but pray the gracious Duke
Sees fit to pardon you.'

The Duke did spare old Shylock's life
Despite the havoc wrought,
He told Shylock he could go –
He hurried from the court.

Then everyone thanked Portia
And said, 'Don't rush away.'
But she replied most graciously
That she really couldn't stay.

'We must reward you,' they all said,
'For everything you've done.'
Portia refused but then she saw
How to have some fun.

And turning to Bassanio said,
'Please give me just one thing –
By way of a small keepsake
Let me have that lovely ring.

'Then I shall not forget today
As long as I may live.'
Bassanio said gravely,
'It's the one thing I can't give.'

He said, 'I cannot part with this,
A gift from my dear wife,
For I gave her a solemn vow
'Twould stay with me for life.'

Portia replied that her request
Was such a little thing;
So, feeling very guilty,
He handed her the ring.

Portia returned to Belmont,
Glad she'd sorted out the mess;
On arriving back at home
She put on normal dress.

When the others came to Belmont
They were a merry band,
They talked about the lawyer
Who'd lent such a helping hand.

Then Portia said, 'Bassanio,
You know it's a funny thing,
There's something strange about you...
Oh yes – where's your wedding ring?'

Poor Bassanio then explained
How he'd given it away,
He said the bright young lawyer
Would not take any pay.

'He said he wanted just the ring.
How could I refuse his plea
After all he'd done to help?
'Twas all he'd take from me.'

Portia smiled and sweetly said,
'Take this new one then I pray.'
Bassanio saw the ring she held
Was the one he gave away.

Said Portia, 'I'm the lawyer
Who saved Antonio's life.'
Bassanio, in amazement,
Hugged his resourceful wife.

He said, 'My dear, forgive me
And I promise you one thing:
Never again will I lose sight
Of my precious wedding ring.'

Then Portia laughed and kissed him
And to Antonio said,
'There's fantastic news for you,
In this letter I've just read.

'Your ships have come back safely,
They're tied up at Venice quay.'
Antonio raised his arms and said,
'What wonderful news for me!'

They laughed and were so thankful
Things had turned out this way.
Then Portia said, 'Time now for bed –
It's very nearly day.'

They left Benedick behind
To ponder what he'd heard

MUCH ADO ABOUT NOTHING

Much ado about nothing
Is the title of this ruse,
But don't be fooled, dear reader,
There's much here to amuse.

Our tale starts in Messina
With two beautiful young girls,
Who we'll come to know quite well
As our tale of love unfurls.

The first one was called Beatrice;
She was happy, light and gay,
Hero was the other,
Much more serious in her way.

They lived with Leonato
In a happy state of peace,
Shy Hero was his daughter,
Witty Beatrice his niece.

Leonato was the Governor
Of the lush lands all around,
And to his every whim and word
The peasants all were bound.

One day the girls on looking
From their palace window saw,
A troop of high-born soldiers
Just returning from a war.

Young and bold and handsome,
In the war they'd all fought well;
Each one had acted bravely
And had many a tale to tell.

Among them was Don Pedro,
Bold leader at their helm.
He was Lord of Arragon,
A high prince of the realm.

And with him was young Claudio,
The Prince's special friend,
And Benedick – known for his wit
That seemed to have no end.

All these courageous soldiers
Had been here once before –
This was several months ago,
On their way to fight the war.

On arriving they discussed
All that had happened since;
Benedick was speaking to
Leonato and the Prince.

Then Beatrice said to Benedick
In a sly, sarcastic way,
'I'm amazed you are still talking
As no-one heeds what you say.'

Benedick was most displeased
Since this came from one so young,
He thought a well-bred lady
Should have a more civil tongue.

He thought and then remembered
She'd made jibes like this before,
And here she was now playing
Silly games on him once more.

'What then, my Lady Beatrice,
Can it be you're still alive?'
He looked at her with great disdain,
Indifference to contrive.

Now once again they argued
As they had done in the past,
Their wit it bounded back and forth,
Both furious and fast.

She said, 'I'll eat those you have killed
And I'll do it just for fun.'
She said this to imply of course
He'd not killed anyone.

Allowing not a moment
To let her insult fester,
She added Benedick was just
The Prince's unpaid jester.

He ignored the first insult,
For he knew that he was brave,
He had proved so many times
How a soldier should behave –

But when she called him jester
It was the worst slur, forsooth,
A little near the knuckle,
A bit too close to the truth.

The Prince saw them quarrelling
And to Leonato said,
'Oh what fun if we could get
That bickering pair to wed.'

He pointed to them saying,
'Would that not make you glad?'
Smiling, Leonato said,
'They'd drive each other mad.'

Though old Leonato thought
They'd only make bad weather,
The Prince would not forsake his plan
To bring the two together.

Meanwhile Claudio admired
Shy Hero from afar,
He thought she was quite lovely,
A bright and shining star.

So later he addressed the Prince,
He wanted him to know,
How he adored fair Hero,
How much he loved her so.

The Prince approved the match and asked
Leonato to agree,
Leonato said, 'Of course,
'Twould bring great joy to me.'

So Claudio asked Hero
To consent to be his bride,
She said she'd be delighted
To spend life at his side.

Claudio wished to marry then
And do it in great style,
But he was told he must postpone
His wedding for a while.

And so to help to pass the time
For this young impatient man,
The Prince outlined what he was sure
Would be a fun-filled plan.

His idea was the men would all
Make Benedick believe
That Beatrice was in love with him –
What a playful web to weave!

Then Hero would get Beatrice
Worked up and in a stir,
And make her think that Benedick
Was now in love with her.

They picked an ideal moment
When Benedick was seated,
Alone among the garden walks
Where sometimes he retreated.

Then Leonato and the Prince
Keeping out of sight,
Began a conversation
That was casual and light.

'Leonato,' said the Prince,
'Now tell me – didn't you say,
That Beatrice loved Benedick
In the most passionate way?

'I didn't think that she could love
Or tolerate a man.'
'Nor I,' said Leonato,
'But now it seems she can.'

The gentlemen moved off,
The Prince had said his final word,
They left stunned Benedick behind
To ponder what he'd heard.

He had listened carefully.
'Can this be true?' said he.
'Can fiery Lady Beatrice
Be so in love with me?

'It's very hard to credit
As she's always so aloof,
But if they're both convinced – well then
I guess it is the truth.

'I never thought to marry
But now love has alighted,
The fervent love of Beatrice
Must surely be requited.

'For she is very virtuous
As any fool can see,
And truly wise in everything,
Save in her love for me.

'But wait – here comes good Beatrice,
And I think I do espy
Her look of ardour shining bright –
I know the reason why.'

'I have been sent to tell you
That we're about to dine.'
Benedick mouthed a *Thank you*,
Said, 'The pleasure is all mine.'

Though she responded tartly
And seemed quite out of reach,
He thought he felt some kindness
Beneath her sharp-tongued speech.

⁂

Now Benedick was fully snared,
He'd given his poor heart;
It then became young Hero's turn
To play a crucial part.

She sent for the two ladies
Who attended to her needs,
For both of them were loyal
In their words and in their deeds.

'Good, sweet Margaret,' Hero said,
'Run to the parlour please,
Tell Beatrice to look for me
In the garden by the trees.

'Tell her I am with Ursula –
She should steal upon us there –
We'll be beneath the oaks and elms...
Tell her exactly where.

'Tell her she'll hear some secrets
She never will believe,
Things beyond her wildest dreams,
Things she could not conceive.'

Margaret did as she was bid;
Beatrice fell for the plan.
On approaching she could hear
Them talking of a man.

And so she hid and listened
As she heard Ursula say,
'Are you sure?' – then Hero said,
'I heard it yesterday.

'Claudio and the Prince both said
That Benedick loves her well,
They asked me to acquaint her
But I said I'd never tell.

'I told them if they were his friends
They mustn't let her know,
If Beatrice knew he loved her,
How she would tease him so.'

They then strolled off upon their way
Leaving Beatrice all agog,
For she could not believe she'd heard
This astounding dialogue.

'My ears are all on fire,' she cried,
'Can this be really true?
Farewell to scorn, contempt and pride,
I bid them all adieu.

'Oh dear Benedick, love on,
Best man in all the land,
I will requite your tender love
With this, my loving hand.'

And now we reach the point at which
You quickly will discern,
Our story is about to take
A most distressing turn.

The Prince had a half-brother,
He bore the title Don,
He was a nasty person
And went by the name of John.

He loathed the Prince, his brother,
With a hatred without end,
And likewise hated Claudio
Who was the Prince's friend.

He planned to stop the marriage,
He would take any measure;
His one and only reason being
For malicious pleasure.

Don John employed a villain,
Borachio was his name:
To ruin Hero's honour
Was their mean, artful game.

Borachio courted Margaret
Hero's young and naive maid.
Listen now most carefully
How this nasty plot was laid.

He asked the simple Margaret
To go that very night,
To Hero's bedroom window
And just stand there in the light;

To dress in Hero's clothes and thus
Enhance her normal style,
To meet him there alone
And chat with him awhile.

Don John then summoned Claudio
And the Prince – and to them said,
'Young Hero talks to strangers
While all others are abed.

'Come with me this very night,
You'll see what I have seen,
Come to her chamber window
And witness what I mean.'

Claudio said, 'I'll shame her,
I swear it on my life,
If I find there's a reason
Why she shouldn't be my wife.'

So that night Don John took them
At the dark appointed hour,
To wait and watch in hiding
Beneath fair Hero's bower.

There they beheld Borachio,
Which cut them to the core,
For with him was fair Hero –
That's what they *thought* they saw.

Now Claudio and the Prince
Were completely taken in,
They were convinced that Hero
Had committed carnal sin.

Claudio felt an anger
That nothing would allay;
How *could* his Hero do this
Just before their wedding day.

His love then turned to hatred
And he vowed he would besmirch
Her virtuous reputation
The following day in church.

Next day they all assembled
For the wedding – and the feast.
Young Claudio and his bride to be
Stood there before the priest.

Then Claudio accused her
In the most fearful way.
'Why do you speak such words,' she cried,
'On this our wedding day?'

Leonato asked the Prince,
'Good Sir, why speak not you?'
'Because the girl's not worthy,
What Claudio says is true.

'We saw her cheating,' said the Prince.
'Such an unseemly sight,
Alone with a strange gentleman
In her room at dead of night.'

At this poor Hero fainted
On the church's stone-flagged floor,
While Claudio and the angry Prince
Strode coldly out the door.

Benedick and Beatrice knelt
Each side of Hero's head.
'Is she all right?' he asked her,
'I fear she's dead,' she said.

Now Beatrice did not believe
A word of what she'd heard,
But poor old Leonato
Accepted every word.

He stooped beside his daughter
Crying out the poor child's name,
Quite borne down with sorrow
And an overpowering shame.

But the honest, ancient priest
Was a clever man indeed,
Sharp were his observations,
And merciful his creed.

And as he'd seen fair Hero
Colour up, then simply wilt,
These symptoms had convinced him
She was free of any guilt.

He said to Leonato,
'Though this now seems so appalling,
You can call me an old fool,
Ignore my age and calling,

'But I swear I've never seen
Such outright, blameless terror;
I'm certain there's no guilt here,
But just a shameful error.'

When Hero had recovered
The kind priest said to her:
'Who is this man they talk of?'
She replied, 'I know not, sir.'

Then Hero said, 'Oh father,'
In a voice quite out of breath,
'If this is true, then hate me,
Even have me put to death.'

But the priest spoke out again,
'There's much confusion here,
Young Claudio and the Prince
Must have got it wrong I fear.'

Turning to Leonato
With a weary gaze he said,
'I think it best that for a while
We say that Hero's dead.'

'How will that help matters?'
Leonato up and cried.
'What will become of all of this
If we say Hero's died.'

'Good will emerge,' the priest replied.
'Just put your trust in me.
Slander will to pity turn
I'm sure that's what we'll see.

'When Claudio hears his love has died
I think that you will find
Fond thoughts of Hero's sweetness
Will creep into his mind.'

Benedick remarked, 'He's right,
It's the only thing to do.'
Leonato sighed – 'Oh well,
I'll leave it up to you.'

Then taking Hero by the hand
The priest led her away.
Benedick said to Beatrice,
'What an awful wedding day!'

'Oh for a man,' cried Beatrice,
'Who'd right this wrong for me,
Who'd clear my dear, sweet Hero's name
For all the world to see.'

Benedick cried with feeling,
'What would you have me do?
I'll do anything you want
To prove my love for you.

'Tell me what to do,' he begged.
(He was a man possessed)
'Kill Claudio,' she shouted;
Beatrice was most distressed.

'Not for anything,' said he,
His face blanched ghostly white,
'She's made him look an utter fool,
It's he who's in the right.'

'Were I a man,' she cried,
Her voice shaking in its pain,
'I'd see your fine friend Claudio
Was well and truly slain.

'What fancy words you do declaim,
What empty threats you make –
Oh for a man who'd help me
Right this wrong for Hero's sake.

'All I see are men so full
Of selfish, proud deceiving,
Why can't I find a decent man
To ease a woman's grieving?'

'Enough then!' Benedick exclaimed,
'I'll challenge him for you;
Claudio will pay the price
Before this day is through.'

Meanwhile poor Leonato
Thought his good name defiled,
And challenged Claudio outright
For the honour of his child.

He said, 'Come, sir – take up your sword
So I can run you through.'
'Nay, nay, old man' his foe replied,
'I will never fight with you.'

Then furious Benedick appeared,
His sword clasped in his hand,
And boldly challenged Claudio:
'Draw sword and make a stand.'

But Claudio knew immediately
What must have happened here.
''Tis Beatrice has done this,' he said,
'Put you up to this, I fear.'

And yet he took the challenge
And would have fought his friend
If something hadn't happened
To bring things to an end.

A magistrate came on the scene,
Borachio at his side;
He told them how Borachio
And bad Don John had lied.

The villain's conversation
By others had been heard;
He had condemned himself and John
With every nasty word.

His guilt was all too certain,
Transparent through and through,
He'd boasted of Don John's design
And what he'd had to do.

He now came clean, and told the truth,
And freely did confess,
That he had been with Margaret
Who'd worn young Hero's dress.

And any doubt that still remained
For anyone or other
Was soon dispelled when news came in
Don John had fled his brother.

Claudio was sorely grieved,
He wrung his hands and cried,
Because he'd wronged sweet Hero
And now the girl had died.

He said, 'Dear Leonato,
Forgive my wrong to you,
And any penance that you choose
I will most gladly do.'

Leonato said with sadness,
'My daughter being dead,
You and sweet Hero's cousin
Must now be wed instead.'

Claudio agreed to this
To give him some relief,
He'd do anything to ease
Poor Leonato's grief.

Claudio still loved Hero,
His heart was full of sorrow,
But he resolved to marry
This stranger on the morrow.

Next day the Prince escorted
Claudio to his wedding,
Though this was truly an event
Poor Claudio was dreading.

Leonato brought his niece,
She stood right by his side,
And Claudio bowed his head
To his second promised bride.

The lady wore a snowy mask
Of finest opaque lace,
To make quite sure that Claudio
Could not observe her face.

Claudio said, 'Fair lady,
Give me your hand, I ask.'
'I will,' replied the stranger,
And then took off her mask.

It was no stranger hidden
Behind the lacy mesh,
But Claudio's own dear Hero
Who stood there in the flesh.

Claudio saw that he had been
The victim of their lies,
But he was simply overjoyed,
Could not believe his eyes.

The Prince asked, 'Is this Hero,
For she appears to thrive?'
'She died,' Leonato answered,
'While her slander was alive.'

'I will explain,' the priest then said,
'How she was hidden away,
But not till this young couple
Have enjoyed their wedding day.'

He was about to carry on
When Benedick up and said,
'I'm in love with Beatrice
And we also wish to wed.'

So Benedick and Beatrice
Were married with their friends,
And with this great occasion
It is here our story ends.

Except to say that evil John
Was brought to book in time,
And taken to Messina
To be punished for his crime.

And so they all lived happily
Once the four of them were wed,
And it had all been much ado
About nothing – as we said!

A splendid ship was fighting hard
To flee a watery grave

THE TEMPEST

Free your mind of everything,
Let imagination fly,
Soar with me above the sea
Come and fly across the sky.

To an island that is lapped
By gentle, turquoise water,
Where an old man, Prospero,
Lives with his only daughter.

The girl is called Miranda
And her memory has no trace
Of other human features
Beyond her father's face.

For she was young when they arrived,
They live there all alone;
So life with her old father
Is the only life she's known.

Prospero studied magic
And through this had come to know,
An ancient witch had lived close by
Who'd died some time ago.

This hag was known as Sycorax;
She'd thought it quite a wheeze,
To lock up kindly spirits
In the bodies of large trees.

When Prospero had learned of this
On coming to the isle,
He'd used his magic to release
The spirits from their trial.

These gentle, kindly spirits
Overcome with great relief,
All grew to love the wizard,
As did Ariel – their chief.

Blessed with a charming nature,
He was humorous and light,
Full of boundless energy,
A lively little sprite.

Alas, he had but one grave fault
Which no-one there could budge,
He'd tease an ugly monster
Against whom he held a grudge.

This poor soul was Caliban –
Whatever had he done?
Well, the witch had been his mother,
He her only son.

When Prospero discovered him
He thought he was an ape,
He had such funny movements
And a very funny shape.

Prospero had rescued him
For he was cold and weak,
He'd shown him many kinds of things
And taught him how to speak.

But Caliban was not inclined
To work hard and be good,
Although they gave him easy tasks
Like gathering up their wood.

He could be very lazy
And didn't care to work,
But Ariel would ensure that he
Had little chance to shirk.

Ariel could not be seen,
Except by Prospero's eyes,
So he would pinch poor Caliban
And then ignore his cries.

He'd sometimes turn into an ape
Which Caliban could see,
For Ariel could take the shape
Of what he wished to be.

He might become a hedgehog
With spikes that puncture skin,
And bumping into Caliban
Would try to prick his shin.

So he'd torment the monster
And Caliban would rue
The days he didn't do the tasks
That he'd been told to do.

Prospero made the spirits
All subservient to him;
They would carry out requests,
Indulge his every whim.

And through them he could order
An extravagant decree,
Which would control the fickle winds
And rule waves of the sea.

Performing these amazing feats
Became for him the norm,
So it was nothing special
When one day he raised a storm.

And in this most tremendous storm,
Caught in a mighty wave,
A splendid ship was fighting hard
To flee a watery grave.

He showed this to his daughter:
She said, 'Pity their distress.'
There was no doubt that Prospero
Had got them in a mess.

'Dear father, save their souls!' she cried.
'Oh, let them all be saved.'
Miranda was in quite a state –
She shouted, cried and raved.

'Don't be afraid my daughter,
There's no cause to be alarmed,
I have arranged the tempest so
That no-one will be harmed.'

Then Prospero continued,
'I know the storm looks wild,
But I have manufactured it
For you, my only child.

'You know not where you came from,
You know just what you see,
You know I am your father
But that's all you know of me.

'Now say, do you remember
Of a time before this place?'
Then, thinking carefully, she said,
'I just recall a trace.'

'I'm not surprised,' he answered.
'As you know I've often told
Of how when we first came here
You were only three years old.'

Miranda said, 'It's very faint
But now and then it seems,
I have a recollection,
When I'm sleeping – in my dreams.

'I think I am surrounded
By maids – I can't be sure.'
Prospero went on quietly,
'Can't you remember more?'

'No dear father,' she replied,
'That's really all I can.'
He said, 'Before we came here
I was Duke of fair Milan.

'You were a princess and enjoyed
A life devoid of care,
As my one and only child
You would one day be my heir.

'I had a younger brother
I'd have trusted with my life,
He lifted from my shoulders
All the daily toil and strife.

'So I retired to study
And avoided many cares,
For Antonio, your uncle,
Looked after my affairs.

'But he was acting falsely,
As soon I was to find,
While I was busy working
To improve my mind.

'As he had all the power
He was very quick to think,
That he himself should be the Duke –
It happened in a wink.

'He planned to take my Dukedom –
Yes, he really stooped that low –
And with the King of Naples,
Who was my most deadly foe,

'He laid a devious plan
To take everything I had,
I know it's hard to credit
But he really was that bad.

'He took us then aboard a ship
And we went out to sea,
And once we were some miles from land,
That's when he set us free.

'With neither tackle nor a sail
He placed us in a boat,
And then he cast us off to drift
Just aimlessly afloat.

'By luck my friend, Gonzalo,
A kind and noble Lord,
Had seen that food and water –
And my books – were placed on board.

'We drifted willy nilly
For so many countless miles.
I was kept from giving up
By your happy, childish smiles.

'Our food gave out just at the point
We landed safely here.
There you have the history
Of our misfortunes, dear.'

'Now father,' kind Miranda said,
'Take trouble to explain,
The reason for the tempest,
Why this mighty wind and rain.'

'By this storm,' her father said,
'I'm able to make sure,
These foes of whom I spoke will now
Be washed up on our shore.

'My brother sails upon that ship,
The King of Naples too;
This wicked pair tried to destroy
Not only me, but you.'

Prospero on looking up
Saw Ariel standing there,
So lest Miranda think that he
Was speaking to thin air...

He touched her with his magic wand,
And then without a peep
Her head inclined upon her chest
And she fell fast asleep.

'Well, spirit,' Prospero said,
'These questions would I ask:
Have you done all I wished and how
Have you performed your task?'

Ariel told him of the storm
And the fear of those on board,
How all of them were fighting hard
As the mighty tempest roared.

'The king's own son, Prince Ferdinand,
Jumped straight into the sea;
The king believes his son is lost,
But he's resting on our quay.

'He is praying,' Ariel said,
'His father will be found,
But inside he really thinks
His father has been drowned.

'No hair upon his head is hurt,
He's fine – all this I saw –
His princely robes are wet, it's true,
But cleaner than before!'

'Gentle Ariel,' Prospero said,
'Now he has had a rinse,
Bring him to meet Miranda,
For she must see this prince.

'And tell me what has happened
To the king and to my brother?'
'They're searching for Prince Ferdinand
While they console each other.

'Although they think they saw him drown
Beneath a mighty wave,
They cannot quite accept he may
Have found a watery grave.

'The crew are safe though each believes
Himself the last alive,
And I've ensured the ship will ride
The storm and still survive.

'I'll guide it to our harbour;
I trust this pleases you?'
'It does indeed,' good Prospero said,
'But there's more work to do.'

'More work!' cried Ariel in alarm,
'You know you promised me,
If I gave loyal service,
You would gladly set me free.'

Prospero said: 'Why, what is this?
Remember when we met,
I saved you from vile Sycorax –
How quickly you forget.'

'Forgive me my dear master,
Pay no heed to my demands,
I'm not at all ungrateful –
What are your new commands?'

'Obey me,' Prospero replied.
'Do all these things for me;
You'll see I'll keep my promise then
And I *will* set you free.'

He told the spirit next to check
On how the young prince fared.
When Ariel discovered him
He looked both tense and scared.

'Oh brave young man,' the spirit thought,
'I'll soon move you along.'
And losing not a moment
He began to sing a song.

Ferdinand sat bolt upright
On hearing this strange singing,
Then followed the sweet music
With both his ears a-ringing.

Ariel's voice was beautiful;
It sang both high and low,
And led the prince towards the girl
And her father, Prospero.

Miranda looking up beheld
Something that made her ponder.
Prospero said, 'Now tell me, child,
What takes your fancy yonder?'

She said, 'Is that a spirit?
It has such lovely features,
Oh father, it is surely
The most beautiful of creatures.'

'He's no spirit,' Prospero said,
'He's just like you and I –
He eats and sleeps and breathes like us
And like us too will die.

'This youth was travelling aboard
The tempest stricken ship,
He has been saved but not before
He took a little dip.

'And although there is no doubt
He's very much relieved,
He thinks his friends are lost and so
He's also much aggrieved.'

Miranda thought the handsome prince
A passion-stirring sight,
And as she looked her tender heart
Was filled with pure delight.

Ferdinand when he looked up
And saw her lovely face
Could not believe what he beheld
In this forsaken place.

He thought the isle enchanted,
'You're a goddess!' he then said.
'I'm but a maid,' she answered,
As she turned the brightest red.

Prospero was very pleased,
She'd met her shining knight,
And it was clear that both of them
Had found true love on sight.

But Prospero still had to test
The prince's love was true,
He called him 'Spy' and threatening said,
'I'll teach you what to do.

'You'll follow me,' he fiercely said.
'I'll tie you, neck and feet;
You'll drink the water from the sea,
And roots are all you'll eat.'

'Indeed, I won't,' cried Ferdinand.
He drew his sword and said,
'You try to force these things on me
And you might end up dead.'

But Prospero waved his wand and so
A magic spell was sown –
In half a second Ferdinand
Was frozen like a stone.

Miranda cried aloud, for thoughts
Of love were in her head.
'Why are you so ungentle?
Oh, have pity, sir,' she said.

'This is the only man I've seen
Except, of course, for you,
And he seems to me to be
As steady as he's true.

'I will vouch for him,' she said –
Her heart was in a whirl.
'Be silent,' said her father,
'Or I'll punish you, my girl.

'You think that he has qualities
Which others can't display?
You're being very headstrong
To speak in such a way.

'You have never had the chance
To know another man;
This youth might be no better than
Our servant, Caliban.'

Prospero was a cunning man,
A wise and keen observer;
He did these things to test her love,
Her constancy and fervour.

He wasn't disappointed –
She was in a state of bliss;
She said, 'I do not wish to know
A better man than this.'

Prospero held the captive prince
In a dark and dismal cave,
Till Ferdinand began to feel
That he'd become a slave.

He felt this even more so
When released from his dank cell
And given a hard and menial job –
Which he found to be sheer hell.

It was a heavy task, and yet
He did as best he could:
Prospero instructed him
To pile great logs of wood.

When Prospero told his daughter
What young Ferdinand was doing,
She said she would be happier
If he had been a-wooing.

Prospero then took his leave
At least he vanished into air.
Miranda then approached the prince,
She said, 'This isn't fair.

'Do not toil so hard,' she said,
'Father's now at work.'
But he replied, 'I must do this,
I really dare not shirk.'

'I'll help you then,' the girl replied.
'You rest here by this tree.'
But there was nothing that would make
Prince Ferdinand agree.

As they began to talk the work
Of stacking logs slowed down,
And when he asked her for her name
Miranda gave a frown.

For Prospero had warned her
Not to tell the prince her name,
But this was part and parcel
Of her father's little game.

Prospero heard her give it,
For he stood there by her side:
The wizard was invisible –
He had no need to hide.

And when he heard his daughter
Disobey him this one time,
He wasn't angry with her
For this paltry little crime.

And when he heard the prince declare
He loved her far above
All other women in the world,
He blessed him for his love.

Happy that the prince now yearned
For Miranda's touch,
Happy that young Ferdinand
Was in love so very much.

She said, 'I know no others,
But I know one thing is true:
I do not wish for anyone
In all the world but you.'

At this her father nodded
In a way as if to say:
'I see my girl will be the Queen
Of Naples one fine day.'

And then Miranda said, 'Good sir,
I will, if you are free,
Become your loving wife, if you
Would care to marry me.'

Before the prince could answer
With all that filled his head,
Prospero materialised
In front of them and said,

'Do not be afraid my child
That I have overheard,
For I approve most readily
Of every single word.

'And Ferdinand, now leave the logs,
Enjoy a well-earned rest,
The tasks I set were but a trial –
You've nobly passed the test.

'Take my daughter as my gift,
It's what I truly sought,
And it's what your loving heart
Has just as truly bought.'

He said he now had things to do,
He'd leave them all alone,
And they, of course, were very pleased
To be there on their own.

Prospero summoned Ariel
And asked him one more thing:
'What of my selfish brother
And his feckless friend, the king?'

Ariel said he'd left them
Almost overcome with fear,
Because of the mysterious things
He'd caused them both to hear.

He'd conjured up a banquet
To appear before their eyes,
Then turned into a monster,
Just by way of a disguise.

He caused the feast to vanish
And to their amazement said,
'It's you who left poor Prospero
And his little girl for dead.'

They cried in fear and terror
And declared, 'It wasn't me.'
He said, 'You left the both of them
To perish out at sea.

'And this is now the reason
That you're suffering in this way.'
Then both of them repented
What they did that awful day.

And Ariel told his master
That he could not help but feel,
That what they'd said was from the heart,
Sincere and very real.

'Bring them here then,' Prospero said,
'For I'm inclined to fashion
A neat solution to this mess
And show them some compassion.'

Ariel straight away brought back
Antonio and the king,
They were both confused
And couldn't understand a thing.

They also were afraid and quite
Borne down with grief and woe,
And neither recognised
Milan's Duke – Prospero.

Gonzalo too was with them –
You will recall I wrote,
How he had helped poor Prospero
By fitting out the boat.

So Prospero revealed himself
To Gonzalo first of all,
And calling him 'my dearest friend'
He asked him to recall,

How he had helped him to survive
A voyage filled with strife,
And said he was his truest friend
Because he'd saved his life.

Antonio and the chastened king
Both bowed down very low,
For now they saw before them
The ill-treated Prospero.

'Forgive me!' begged Antonio
On his knees, time after time;
The king said he was sorry
For assisting with the crime.

Prospero forgave them both,
He was a kindly man,
And they agreed that once again
He should rule Milan.

Then Prospero showed the king his son
Who, with Miranda there,
Was calmly playing chess, as if
They didn't have a care.

The king was quite bewildered
Although overcome with joy –
He scarcely could believe that here
He'd found his own dear boy.

They hugged each other saying,
'This surely cannot be.'
As each had thought the other
Was forever lost at sea.

'Oh wonder!' said Miranda.
'Who are these lovely creatures?
What a gorgeous world to have
Such people with such features.'

The king was quite astonished
By Miranda's lovely face,
He said, 'Who is this beauteous maid
With charm and boundless grace?'

'This lady,' Ferdinand replied,
'So beautiful and fine,
Has smiled on me today and has
Consented to be mine.

'I could not ask permission
As I thought that you were dead,
But now with your fond blessing
We are planning to get wed.

'And she is Prospero's daughter,
The ruler of Milan,
He'll be my second father,
A worthy, upright man.'

Then with emotion running high,
They each one hugged the other,
And Prospero again forgave
His wicked, erring brother.

Antonio was quite borne down
With shame and deep remorse.
Gonzalo wept outright to see
Events take such a course.

Prospero said, 'The ship is safe
With all of those on board.'
Then offered them the finest meal
His island could afford.

He called on Caliban to serve
A lavish, tasty feast.
The company were all amazed
To see this monstrous beast.

Prospero called to Ariel:
'You've been very true to me,
And as I've always promised,
I'm going to set you free.'

Later Prospero buried
In a dark and hidden nook,
His trusty wand, his potions
And his special magic book.

He now resolved that he would make
A new and better start,
Renouncing altogether
Any practice of his art.

Reunited with his brother
And also with the king,
His heart was full of gladness
And took joy in everything.

And eager to return at last
Unto his native land,
He had the ship made ready
For this very happy band.

Ariel was so grateful now
To be completely free,
And as he still loved Prospero
Watched the ship set out to sea.

In gratitude for all the time
That they had spent together,
He calmed the sea to guarantee
The ship enjoyed fine weather!

A friendly, though a dismal look
In its red, rheumy eye

HAMLET, PRINCE OF DENMARK

This tale is set in Denmark
Back in dismal days of old,
And is a tale of mayhem
Like no other ever told.

It begins just two months after
Old King Hamlet's final breath,
Which shocked the Danish court
As his had been a sudden death.

And then his widow Gertrude
Giving wifely grief no time,
Had done a deed that many thought
Was virtually a crime.

She'd wed her husband's brother,
It was quite the strangest thing,
For now she was the brother's wife
They had to crown him king.

Now Claudius, the brother,
Was a most unpleasant kind;
He was devoid of goodness
In both character and mind.

Some thought he'd slain his brother
So that he could take his place,
But now he was the king, of course,
None said this to his face.

Before this sorry marriage,
Before this seed was sown,
The old king's son, Prince Hamlet,
Had been heir to Denmark's throne.

Hamlet who'd loved his father –
Idolized him, some would say –
Could not forgive his mother
For her second wedding day.

He hated her new husband
And, ashamed of what she'd done,
Became borne down with sadness,
His life devoid of fun.

He grew weary of the world,
He couldn't understand,
What had possessed his mother
To accept his uncle's hand.

How *could* she choose his uncle
To share her marital bed?
He felt this hurt inside him,
But it all remained unsaid.

Of course his mother's marriage
Meant that he had lost the throne,
A matter now of small concern
As he wandered round alone.

As Hamlet paced the castle,
Thinking how to make things right,
He heard of how the guards had seen
A ghost at dead of night.

The ghost was Hamlet's father –
It was truly the dead king –
It walked the walls at midnight,
Such a terrifying thing.

It looked forlorn and pale and wan,
Its face a mask of sorrow,
It disappeared the moment
The cock crowed out the morrow.

Hamlet wished to see the ghost
To ease his troubled heart,
For he reasoned it might have
A message to impart.

There must be a reason why
It walked the walls at night;
Surely it did not appear
Just to give the guards a fright.

So one dark night he waited
For the spirit to appear,
He felt deep dread and anguish
As his father's ghost drew near.

But then Hamlet's courage grew
As he thought he did espy,
A friendly, though a dismal, look
In its red, rheumy eye.

It seemed it wished to speak to him,
Though Hamlet would have rather
Run the other way – he spoke
'Oh Hamlet, King – oh father.'

The ghost turned to Prince Hamlet
And looked him in the face,
Then he beckoned to his son
To find a quiet place.

Now Hamlet's good companions were
Most worried for their friend;
They feared that the noble prince
Might meet a sticky end.

They tried their best to hold him back
But Hamlet broke away,
He was now intent to hear
All the ghost would have to say.

The ghost – once they were all alone
Turned to his son and said,
'Yes – I am your father
Whom you know is really dead.

'I am truly his poor ghost.
Now please take special heed –
While I tell you of treachery
And of an awful deed.

'I was murdered, my dear son
In the most atrocious way.
It happened in my garden,
As I slept there one day.

'Claudius crept up on me,
He made sure I didn't hear,
Then in a trice he poured a phial
Of poison in my ear.

'It coursed through all my body,
A lethal, deadly oil,
It turned my skin into a crust
And caused my blood to boil.

'The pain racked me through and through,
Until death set me free.
But not before I clearly saw
What he had done to me.

'In a stroke my brother claimed
My queen, my throne, my life,
And now he sits upon my throne
And beds my feckless wife.'

The ghost now craved revenge for what
King Claudius had done,
He explained just what he wanted
To his beloved son.

He yearned to have his brother's life,
He wished to see him dead.
'I cannot rest until it's done,'
The ghost then quietly said.

'But please don't hurt your mother,
She was after all my mate,
Leave the heavens to decide
Upon her final fate.'

Now Hamlet felt much braver,
He had quite regained his nerve,
And so he promised faithfully
He'd constantly observe

All that the ghost had asked of him
And see his father right.
Once he had made this promise
The ghost vanished from his sight.

Hamlet resolved, as he stood there
Upon the castle tower,
That he would spend each moment,
Every single waking hour

Thinking only of the deed
The ghost would have him do,
He vowed that he would take revenge
And see the whole thing through.

Hamlet went back to his friends –
Wild thoughts buzzed through his head –
He only told Horatio
Of what the ghost had said.

The meeting with his father
Left Prince Hamlet feeling down,
He walked around in silence
With a very solemn frown.

Everybody thought that he
Had lost his sense of reason.
Little did they realise
That he was planning treason.

He wanted to take action
Against the murdering king,
He wished to have revenge
For this obscene, appalling thing.

Now Hamlet loved a lady
Who was really quite first rate,
Her father was a powerful man,
Chief counsellor of state.

And he was called Polonius,
Ophelia was her name.
Prince Hamlet had declared his love;
She'd said she felt the same.

But now the Prince ignored her,
And his manner was quite bad,
But this was just an act so she
Would also think him mad.

Ophelia excused his moods
Although he was unkind.
She thought that it was all to do
With his poor state of mind.

It's true he was in turmoil
As he thought of the best way
To finish off his uncle,
He must act without delay.

But Claudius had many guards;
It was no easy thing
To get past all these burly men
So he could kill the king.

One day as he was thinking hard
What in the world to do,
A troop of wandering players
Stopped the night whilst passing through.

Hamlet knew and liked them well,
They were a welcome sight;
In the past their many plays
Had filled him with delight.

The play he liked the best of all
Told of the King of Troy,
And thinking of this play he planned
A quite ingenious ploy.

The drama shows the King of Troy,
In a terrifying scene,
Being cruelly murdered – then
The grief of his poor queen.

So Hamlet asked the players
If they'd make a little change;
There was one scene he wanted
Just to slightly rearrange.

He asked the players to perform
A murder in the way
The ghost had so described *his* death,
Upon that fateful day.

Hamlet hoped his uncle
Would get into a lather
When he saw the players act
The death scene of his father.

He hoped the king would then react
In the manner that he sought,
Because the play would be performed
In front of all the court.

He asked the players to prepare
With this one change of scene,
And then along with all the court
Invited king and queen.

They were extremely eager
To accept and watch the play,
So once they were both seated
The plot got under way.

They didn't know the purpose
That the altered scene would serve,
They didn't know how closely
Young Prince Hamlet would observe

Their reaction to the murder
That the crafty prince had planned,
So close to that committed
By his wicked uncle's hand.

The king's face shone with pleasure
But it quickly turned to fear,
When he saw the deadly poison
Poured in a player's ear.

It was so like the foul deed
He himself had carried out
That he leapt onto his feet
And let out a garbled shout.

He said that he was feeling sick
To hide his fear and gloom,
Then in red faced confusion
He hurried from the room.

Hamlet now could clearly see
All the ghost had said was true,
And now he was in turmoil
As he wondered what to do.

He pondered on the happenings
His eyes had clearly seen,
But then received a message
To attend upon the queen.

He hurried to his mother,
She was waiting for her son,
She said the king and she were both
Dismayed at what he'd done.

She hoped that he would talk to her
In order that the king,
Should get a factual account,
Of every little thing.

Polonius was in hiding,
So he could not be seen,
There in the room, but well concealed
Behind a hanging screen.

Polonius wished to overhear
All that the two would say,
Discover what the truth might be
In this most devious way.

He heard the queen scold Hamlet
For the awful thing he'd done;
He heard her shout, 'How can you think,
That sort of thing is fun?

'You have upset your father.'
She meant his uncle – the king;
This comment upset Hamlet
More than any other thing.

'It's you who've upset father
In your haste to be re-wed,
By taking father's brother
Into your marital bed.'

The queen was very frightened,
His voice had a crazy ring,
She cried out for assistance from
Polonius or the king.

A voice replied immediately,
A voice behind the screen,
It sounded from the spot we know
Polonius to have been.

Hamlet thought, 'It is the king,
I'll give him his reward.'
And with one thrust he stabbed the screen
In hatred, with his sword.

There was a cry – then silence –
And then the chilling sound
Of a body as it slumped
Onto the blood-stained ground.

Hamlet pulled the body out.
'Oh foul deed!' his mother said,
For there was old Polonius
And the wretched man was dead.

'A foul deed?' young Hamlet cried.
'No more than any other,
Not as bad as regicide
Then marrying his brother.'

Hamlet spoke out plainly
Of happy, former days
With his departed father,
And his father's noble ways.

'How could you forget,' he asked,
'In so short a space of time,
Then marry with my uncle
Who carried out this crime?'

And then he said, 'I'm sick of you.'
His words came in a rush.
'You have done a deed so foul
That even the heavens blush.'

He showed her pictures of each king,
And cried aloud, 'Look well,
One has a grace and dignity,
The other belongs in hell.'

He asked, 'How can you bear to live
Your soiled, unworthy life?
How in the world can you remain
Your husband's brother's wife

'When you know he foully murdered
Your husband in this way?'
The queen looked down in terror,
There was nothing she could say.

It was as if the very worst
That she had ever feared
Had come to pass when Hamlet said,
'Father's ghost has now appeared.'

The queen could not perceive the ghost,
But Hamlet saw him there,
The queen thought that her son was mad
When he addressed thin air.

The ghost reminded Hamlet
To go easy on his wife.
'If you taunt her in this way
She may well take her life.'

The ghost departed with the words,
'Take care you slay my brother.'
Hamlet said again he would,
Then turned back to his mother.

He said, 'If you are of a mind
To start on some confessing,
You can relieve your tortured soul
And gain your son's good blessing.

'You must no more associate
With Claudius, the new king.'
The queen said she would follow
What he wished in everything.

And added she was sorry
For the way she had offended.
With this agreement sorted out
The conference was ended.

⁂

Prince Hamlet now considered
Everything he had fulfilled,
But most of all he thought about
Polonius, whom he'd killed.

For he had been a decent man,
He'd not deserved to die,
Hamlet thought of his rash deed,
And then began to cry.

Polonius was the father
Of Ophelia, the girl
With whom he'd been in love and who
Had set his heart awhirl.

The death of old Polonius
Now gave the king a reason
To take revenge on Hamlet
For the dangerous crime of treason.

For Claudius wished his brother's son
Would draw his final breath,
In fact he really wanted
To have him put to death.

But the people loved Prince Hamlet
And his mother loved him too,
So there was only just one thing
The evil king could do.

That was to exile Hamlet
To England's distant shore,
For then the king would have no need
To see him anymore.

He sent the prince with two stout guards
He knew would guard him well,
And who could both be trusted,
And would never ever tell

About the deed the king had planned,
The evil end he sought –
To have Prince Hamlet murdered
At the mighty English court.

But on their way to England
The Danish captain spied,
A pirate ship approaching
And they had nowhere to hide.

The pirate ship attacked them
And so Hamlet grabbed his sword;
And when it came right up to them
Quite alone, he jumped aboard.

He fought the pirates bravely,
But then saw to his dismay
The Danish ship he'd been on
Had pulled back and sailed away.

He was the pirate's captive,
But the crew turned out to be
All well-disposed towards him,
And in time they set him free.

They set him down in Denmark
On a dark and lonely shore,
Hamlet then returned to court –
He was shocked by what he saw.

A funeral was taking place –
For Ophelia, his love,
Whose soul through misadventure
Was now in heaven above.

It seemed her father's murder
By her lover Hamlet's hand,
Had upset her in a way
She found too hard to stand.

Her mind was sadly weakened
In a most peculiar way,
As she'd been handing flowers
To the ladies every day.

She'd said, 'They're for my father,
Who, sad to say, is dead.'
They knew that there was something
Not quite right inside her head.

Then one day gathering flowers
By a weeping willow tree,
She'd slipped upon a muddy patch
That she had failed to see.

She'd fallen in deep water
And in her poor mental state
Had failed to swim, and so was drowned –
To die young became her fate.

Hamlet guessed at once just who
The funeral was for,
He softly stepped aside and hid –
And this is what he saw.

The queen threw flowers on the grave.
'Sweets to the sweet!' she said,
'I thought that these bright flowers
Would have strewn your wedding bed.'

The fair maid's death had cut the queen
As keenly as a knife,
She cried, 'You should have lived to be
My dear son Hamlet's wife.'

And then the dead maid's brother
Looked down at the coffin lid,
Laertes was the young man's name
And this is what he did.

He jumped, in his consuming grief,
Into the grave and cried,
'Bury me right here as well –
I feel as though I've died.'

Then Hamlet's grief became too much –
He jumped into the grave.
Laertes, when he saw the prince
Began to shout and rave.

Hamlet had killed his father,
He'd run Polonius through,
And grieving Laertes blamed the prince
For Ophelia dying too.

He grabbed Prince Hamlet by the throat
And they began to fight,
Such violence in a graveyard
Was a most distressing sight.

Courtiers prised the pair apart,
Then pulled them from the grave,
They begged them to be reconciled –
So each of them forgave.

But Claudius now saw his chance
To start on the construction,
Of a plan he hoped would end
In Hamlet's swift destruction.

He slyly said to Laertes,
'Challenge Hamlet to a duel.'
But, of course, his motives
Were both devious and cruel.

He summoned the whole court to see,
He said they must attend,
And then the king gave Laertes
A sword with sharpened end.

Prince Hamlet had a blunted sword
As fencing rules laid down,
So the fight would be unfair
By order of the crown.

Then Laertes placed some poison
On the tip of his sharp sword,
The king smiled as he did it
To show his full accord.

Hamlet thus approached the duel
As if it was just fun,
And the queen had no idea
Of the trap laid for her son.

And so the duel got under way,
A most exciting show,
Until the moment Laertes dealt
The Prince a mortal blow.

His sword pierced Hamlet's shoulder,
It was just a flesh wound – but
The poison would make certain
Hamlet died from this small cut.

So Hamlet fought on bravely,
He saw no need to shirk,
He knew not of the poison
As it took some time to work.

Then in a heated scuffle
Both their swords flew overhead,
In the muddle each retrieved
His opponent's sword instead.

With a thrust, then Hamlet ran
His sword through Laertes' frame;
Now both of them were poisoned
In this very nasty game.

Just then the queen rose up and shrieked,
'I'm poisoned,' Gertrude cried.
Then gasping faintly she collapsed
And horribly she died.

The bowl from which the queen had drunk
Was put there by the king;
He'd placed it there so he could be
Assured of everything.

He'd thought that if young Laertes failed
To kill him in the fight,
Then placing deadly poison in
Prince Hamlet's cup – just might.

Laertes then confessed and said
That Hamlet could not live;
He dropped down on one knee and asked
Prince Hamlet to forgive.

He told him of the poison
And how the king had lied;
Hamlet forgave him for his part –
And then poor Laertes died.

Hamlet saw his end approach
And knew there was one thing
That he must do before he died:
He had to kill the king.

He raised his sword and thrust it
With what force he could impart,
The sword pierced his uncle's chest
But narrowly missed his heart.

Hamlet grabbed the poisoned cup,
'Drink what's left,' he said,
The king saw that he had no choice,
He drank and fell down dead.

With the king dead on the floor
Hamlet's course had now been run;
The task set by his father
Had been well and truly done.

Hamlet now was failing fast;
To Horatio he said,
'Tell the world this story
Once your poor, wronged prince is dead.'

Horatio vowed he would,
His noble prince need have no fears,
And with that this sad prince died;
The room was full of tears.

For Hamlet was a gentle prince,
Noble in everything.
And if he'd lived he would have been
A loved and honoured king.

They had wild eyes, hooked noses,
And white pasty withered skin

MACBETH

Now if you took the trouble
To look back in time and seek,
You'd find there reigned in Scotland
A king, Duncan the Meek.

And also at this time there lived
A great and mighty lord,
A kinsman of the king
Who was handy with his sword.

This was the famous Lord Macbeth,
Who was esteemed at court,
Because of all the many wars
He'd planned and bravely fought.

One day Macbeth was riding,
Returning from a war,
Where he'd fought a fearsome battle
And come out top dog once more.

He was with his old friend Banquo
On this very happy day,
And here it is we meet them
As they make their joyful way.

They were on an open heath
When there suddenly appeared,
Three ugly female figures
Who each seemed to have a beard.

They wore torn and scruffy clothing
And they all looked lank and thin,
They had wild eyes, hooked noses,
And white pasty withered skin.

Macbeth addressed them but it seemed
They did not wish to linger,
And each one laid upon her lips
A mangled, bony finger.

But then the first one spoke these words
And raised her bearded head,
'All hail, Macbeth – all hail to thee,
Thane of Glamis!' she said.

Macbeth was very startled
To be known by hags like these,
It made his blood run icy cold,
Brought shivers to his knees.

Then the second witch spoke up,
She had new words to say,
'All hail, Macbeth – Thane of Cawdor,
As you'll surely be one day.'

And finally the third spoke up –
This was the weirdest thing –
'All hail, Macbeth,' she hoarsely said,
'One day you will be king.'

This prophecy was surely
The strangest ever sown,
The king's young sons were still alive,
Successors to the throne.

Macbeth could not be king unless
King Duncan's sons were dead,
One witch then turned to Banquo
And with wagging finger said,

'Lesser are you than Macbeth
But in your way more great,
Not so happy or so charmed
But this will be your fate:

'You may not reign nor even have
These high and mighty things,
Yet all your heirs shall after you
Become great Scottish kings.'

And then the witches disappeared
As though they'd not been there,
They simply vanished out of sight,
As though they'd turned to air.

Macbeth and Banquo pondered
On this most amazing thing,
And as they did a messenger
Arrived there from the king.

'The king gives you, my Lord Macbeth,'
The herald up and said,
'The title, Thane of Cawdor,
On your deserving head.'

Macbeth was most astonished for
He would now have the name
The witches had predicted,
It was the very same.

And now indeed ambition swelled,
Hope bounded in his mind,
He wondered if, as had been told
In time he'd also find

That he was King of Scotland,
But this thought was quite insane,
And yet he kept on hoping
That one day he just might reign.

Macbeth then said to Banquo,
'Do you think your son will be
The King of Scotland's realm one day
As this has come to me?'

'This hope is vain,' his friend replied,
'Be wary, not unwise;
And do not seek to tempt the fates –
That way disaster lies.'

But now the witch's words possessed
Macbeth, both heart and soul,
And from that moment forward
He made Scotland's throne his goal.

Macbeth then later told his wife
Of all that had occurred,
She thought it quite the strangest thing
That she had ever heard.

She was an evil woman,
Full of malice, greed and hate,
The thought of somehow being queen
Got her in quite a state.

She cared not what they both might do,
She cared not how they lied,
For she would stop at nothing –
No, not even regicide.

Macbeth was most reluctant
To assassinate the king,
But his wife insisted
It was the vital thing.

'It is the only way we'll get
The Scottish throne,' she said.
'Old Duncan's blood must surely flow
Until he's good and dead.

'It is the only way, Macbeth,
It's what we both must do,
The only way we can ensure
The prophecy comes true.'

Now sometimes as a favour
King Duncan found a way,
To visit his nobility,
And make a little stay.

And so it was that he arrived
Before the castle doors
Of brave Macbeth, to recognise
His triumphs in the wars.

He had with him his well-loved sons,
Malcolm and Donalbain,
And some high ranking nobles
With attendants in their train.

The castle was most restful,
A pleasant place to be.
The king exclaimed, 'I am well pleased
With everything I see.'

Lady Macbeth then entered,
But cloaked her evil wiles
With many little courtesies
And wreaths of gracious smiles.

Her attitude was innocent,
She did not seem a fake,
But underneath the smiles there hid
A foul and scheming snake.

As she was calmly planning
How the king would soon be dead,
His Majesty declared, 'I'm tired.
I think I'll go to bed.'

He showered presents on his hosts,
Then went up to his rooms,
Wherein he was attended
By his two most trusted grooms.

At the time when only wolf
And murderer are abroad,
Lady Macbeth lay in her bed
Awake beside her Lord.

She plotted how to kill the king,
She wished to see him dead,
All sorts of foul and evil thoughts
Tossed round within her head.

She would not normally have thought
Of doing such a thing,
But she feared Macbeth had not
The nerve to kill the king.

For though he was ambitious
And could be from time to time
Quite ruthless, he still lacked the grit
To carry out this crime.

And so to Duncan's room she crept;
She said, 'This task is mine.'
The grooms were sound asleep because
She'd plied them both with wine.

There lay Duncan fast asleep,
Tired at his journey's end,
But as she gazed upon him
Her resolve began to bend.

He looked just like her father –
She could no more proceed;
She didn't have the courage
To perform the evil deed.

Returning to the chamber,
She said, 'You do this foul deed.'
Macbeth was most reluctant;
It was she who took the lead.

He knew the crime of murder
Was the very greatest sin,
And also knew that Duncan was
One of his closest kin.

He thought of what a decent man
The king had always been,
How he had never been unkind,
Belligerent or mean.

All his nobles loved him
And his subjects found him fair;
Macbeth had heard that kings like this
Were held in heaven's care.

Because of Duncan's kindness
Macbeth stood in high regard,
To go and murder him right now
Would be so very hard.

The lady saw her husband lean
Towards his better side,
But she would not allow her plans
To be so soon denied.

This fiendish wife did all she could
To quell his deepest fears,
And words of strong persuasion
She poured into his ears.

She said, 'My dear, you must not shirk –
Listen and take good heed,
It only takes a second
And is such an easy deed.

'And this decisive action,
Taken at dead of night,
Will turn us into king and queen –
True royalty by right.'

She called her Lord unworthy
And a coward – base as well,
She said he was too fickle –
Oh, she really gave him hell.

She said it would be easy,
They should treat it as a game;
They'd lay the guilt upon the grooms,
Make sure *they* took the blame.

And so with evil argument
His courage she did feed,
Until he summoned up the nerve
To do the bloody deed.

Macbeth took up the dagger,
And then went where Duncan lay,
But as he stood with knife aloft
Something told him 'Stay!'

He saw another dagger
With its shiny blade laid bare,
This one was dripping drops of blood,
Just hanging in the air.

But when he tried to grasp it
His fingers passed right through,
So he turned back to doing
The foul thing he'd come to do.

He stood above King Duncan
With his shiny evil knife,
And then with fierce and fearful stroke
He took the poor man's life.

And then he heard the weirdest noise,
It really made him leap,
One of the dead king's grooms it was,
Who laughed out in his sleep.

The other cried out, 'Murder!'
Then both of them awoke,
And in the deadly, dark of night
One to the other spoke.

'God bless us!' he exclaimed aloud.
'Amen,' his mate replied.
Macbeth stood like a statue, for
There was nowhere to hide.

Paralysed with fear, he stood
And sweating with the strain,
And then to his relief at last
They fell asleep again.

But next he thought he heard a voice;
'Oh, sleep no more,' it said.
Was this a real person
Or a voice inside his head.

He heard the dreadful sound again:
'Cawdor, sleep no more!' it said,
It seemed to speak of everything
He'd come to fear and dread.

'Glamis has murdered sleep,' it cried,
'Oh, sleep no more, Macbeth.'
Somehow it seemed to herald
All the harbingers of death.

Macbeth returned unto his wife
By whom he was assailed;
She thought he hadn't done the deed,
She thought that he had failed.

But when she saw upon his hands
The blood, she surely knew,
That he had done the awful deed,
And seen the whole thing through.

She sent him now to wash, then took
The dagger by the hilt,
And stained the grooms with streaks of blood
To thus imply their guilt.

The king was found upon the morn,
Blood-stained within his rooms.
At first the blame was squarely placed
Upon the sleepy grooms.

But this was not for long, in fact
It took but little time
For blame to fall upon Macbeth
For this horrific crime.

He clearly had good motive,
And the grooms had little reason –
There was naught for them to gain
By thus committing treason.

Meanwhile Duncan's sons took flight –
'Twas certain death to stay –
They knew their only hope was now
To quickly run away.

Now that the heirs apparent had
So quickly up and flown,
It left Macbeth a clear path
To go and take the throne.

So he became the anointed king,
His wife became queen, too,
So all the witches had foretold
Had come completely true.

Macbeth recalled the witches
Had said some other things:
That Banquo's children after him
Would rule as Scotland's kings.

He found this very hard to bear
Considering what they'd done,
To know that when they died the throne
Would go to Banquo's son.

They had defiled their hands with blood,
Performed a wicked crime,
But Banquo's son would be the king
At some far future time.

'We cannot let this happen,'
Said the power-crazed Macbeth,
'Banquo and his son, Fleance,
Must now be put to death.'

So they arranged a banquet
And invited all the thanes,
It was a truly sumptuous feast,
They took enormous pains.

They did their very best to see
Their guests would be delighted,
And Banquo and his son, Fleance,
Were both of them invited.

But as they travelled to the feast
The two of them were caught
By villains sent by King Macbeth,
And though they bravely fought,

Banquo took a fatal wound
And died in dreadful pain,
But in the scuffle Fleance fled
And lived to fight again.

Back in the royal castle,
At the feast upon that night,
Macbeth was soon about to get
A very serious fright.

He'd told the thanes how much he missed
Dear Banquo, his good friend,
He simply couldn't understand
Why he'd chosen not to spend

The evening at the special feast,
He'd promised to be there.
And as he spoke these artful words
The king walked towards his chair.

As he approached his startled eyes
Saw what he feared the most,
For sitting in the regal chair
Was murdered Banquo's ghost.

Macbeth was a bold man, but
He blanched as he drew near,
His eyes were fixed upon the ghost,
He stared with dreadful fear.

The queen and nobles all beheld
Him stand transfixed and stare,
But all they saw was Scotland's king
Gaze at an empty chair.

The queen at once reproached Macbeth
For acting in this way;
The frightened monarch gave no heed
To what she had to say.

He only looked on Banquo's ghost,
Just that and that alone,
And when he spoke the queen was scared
Their secret would be known.

The guests were all dismissed in case
They thought their king and thane
Had lost his grip upon himself
And gone a bit insane.

Macbeth was in a sorry state,
He couldn't get to sleep.
He tried his best to calm his fears,
But they were far too deep.

His dreams were all of Banquo
And the dire deed he'd done;
He thought of poor King Duncan
And of Fleance, Banquo's son.

He thought he'd seek the witches
For he felt that he'd been cursed,
He thought the time had come for him
To know the very worst.

He sought them out within a cave,
Far on the lonely heath;
They were busy making charms
Of tongues and eyes and teeth.

They used the eyes of toads, the tongues
Of adders, bits of rats;
They used the legs of lizards
And tangled wool from bats.

The gall of goats, the roots of yew,
Encased in graveyard mud,
They boiled it in a cauldron which
They cooled with baboon's blood.

They used this dark and evil brew
To see what was in store,
By reaching wicked spirits
Who then told them what they saw.

The witches asked Macbeth if he
Had come for them to tell
Just what the future held for him
By casting of a spell.

'Cast your spells,' Macbeth replied,
'The future let me see.'
And so they called the spirits up.
They said, 'There will be three.'

The first rose up and called Macbeth,
Told him he should beware:
'Watch for the Thane of Fife, Macduff –
Watch him with greatest care.'

The second spirit then arose
And called him to draw near.
It said, 'No-one can hurt you,
You have nothing more to fear.'

'Then live, Macduff,' he boldly cried,
'For I'll fear you no more;
But wait – perhaps he should be killed,
To make things doubly sure.'

The third then came and softly said,
'The final thing to know,
Is that you're safe till Birnam Wood
Becomes a deadly foe.'

How could a wood become a foe?
These words were strange to hear,
Macbeth cried out, 'Sweet goodness!
I have nothing else to fear.'

For who but God could move a wood?
Good news then for Macbeth.
He said, 'It seems that now I'm safe
From an untimely death.

'But there is more I wish to know,'
Went on that selfish thane.
'Will Banquo's children at some time
In Scotland come to reign?'

As soon as he had said these words
There was a mighty sound.
The black and boiling cauldron
Sank down into the ground.

He heard the sound of music
And saw the strangest things;
He saw eight eerie figures
Resembling Scottish kings;

And then Lord Banquo passed him by,
With bloodied smiling face;
He pointed at the line of kings
As if to make the case,

That these were his posterity
And they would reign one day.
Then with the sound of music
The pageant passed away.

Macbeth then left the witches' cave
With hatred in his head,
He was filled with guilt and fear
And an awful clinging dread.

And then he heard that bold Macduff,
Courageous Thane of Fife,
Had travelled south to England,
Being in fear of his life.

He'd gone to join Lord Malcolm
Who was Duncan's rightful heir,
And he was at the English court
To form an army there.

Macbeth, enraged, now took revenge
Upon the Fife thane's kin.
He now performed an act that some
Declared his greatest sin.

He killed the good thane's wife and child,
(For they'd been left behind.)
And any of Macduff's close kin
His evil men could find.

All these horrific actions
Turned the thanes against Macbeth,
His name became synonymous
With tyranny and death.

Now as the King of Scotland grew
More hated every day,
Macduff and Malcolm's army
Made its slow remorseless way.

It was as King Macbeth prepared
To battle for his life,
That he received a bitter blow –
He lost his evil wife.

She had had some awful dreams –
Hers was a sorry state,
Borne down with overpowering guilt,
The butt of public hate.

Now it was rumoured that the queen,
This evil, murderous wife,
Had at the end despairingly
Taken her own life.

Macbeth himself was tired of life
And he began to crack,
He said, 'If I must die, I'll die
With armour on my back.'

He prepared to meet young Malcolm
As a gallant soldier should,
And then recalled the prophecy
Concerning Birnam Wood.

He would be safe all of the time
The wood stayed in its place;
But then a messenger approached
With fear upon his face.

He said, 'I saw the Birnam Wood
Sway and begin to move.'
Macbeth replied, 'This cannot be.
It's something you must prove.'

The king then rushed to have a look
And this is what he saw:
Birnam Wood was on the move –
He did not stop for more.

He leapt astride his horse and rode
To meet the mighty force.
He now resolved to let events
Take their relentless course.

He knew as he went out to fight
He scarcely had one friend,
He said, 'I am so weary,
I think this is the end.'

The sight of the advancing wood
Is easy to explain,
It was the strategy of one
Who had an agile brain.

Malcolm had told his men to cut
A bough from any tree,
And hold it out in front of them
So their enemy couldn't see

How large a force they were, and what
It was they planned to do;
Thus it was the prophecy
Eventually came true.

And so the battle started
And in the midst of the fight
Macbeth fought on with valour,
A bold and raging sight.

Macduff then saw the murderer
Of his beloved wife,
And now a mighty fight ensued
Each battling for his life.

Macduff cried, 'Tyrant, villain!
Prepare for your last breath.'
And with a mighty effort plunged
His sword into Macbeth.

As Macbeth lay there on the ground,
We see an awful thing,
For Macduff chopped his head right off
To give the lawful king.

Malcolm took King Duncan's throne
Amid the people's cheers,
And everyone lived happily,
Delivered from their fears.

No more horrid murders,
No more dismal deeds of death,
No more destructive wars
And no more kings like King Macbeth!

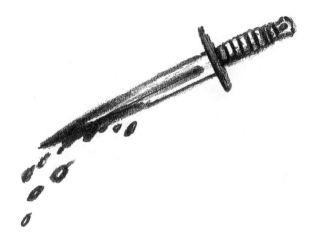

'Why, tell her of my passion,
And of my love,' he said

TWELFTH NIGHT

One fine day in Messaline
In the very early dawn,
With but an hour between them,
Identical twins were born.

One twin was a little boy,
Sebastian was his name;
The girl was called Viola –
The children looked the same.

We'll miss their happy childhood,
And very quickly skip
To one day when they're taking
A long voyage on a ship.

Their vessel hit a heavy storm,
Was tossed and thrown amok,
Until the huge and mighty waves
Sent it crashing on a rock.

Most of the poor souls on board
Were drowned in watery graves;
A few though struggled to a boat
And fought the mighty waves.

Among them was the Captain,
Viola and some crew;
When at last they reached the shore
They were tired and soaked right through.

'It's so hard to be thankful,'
Viola quietly said,
'Not when I know my brother
Is certain to be dead.'

The Captain answered bravely,
'Now don't give up so fast,
I'm sure I saw him clinging to
A piece of broken mast.'

Viola began to hope
Her brother might survive,
There seemed at least a slender chance
He might still be alive.

She wondered then what she could do
In this so foreign land,
And asked the kindly Captain
If he could lend a hand.

'Do you know this place?' she asked,
'Illyria,' he said.
'It was very close to here
That I was born and bred.'

'And can you tell me also
Who's the ruler of this place?'
'A noble Duke,' was his reply,
'Known for kindness and for grace.

'His name is Duke Orsino,
He's respected far and wide,
And he remains a bachelor,
He's never found a bride.

'But that was now a month ago,
'Twas then I last came here,
And at that time there was much talk
Of a lady he holds dear.

'She is called Olivia –
They say he loves her so –
She's the daughter of a Count
Who died twelve months ago.

'Her home was with her brother,
But he died and so, since then,
The lady has lived all alone
And will not speak to men.'

Viola shared the self-same fate
As this quite unknown other
In that she also mourned the loss
Of a departed brother.

She thought perhaps that she could live
With this unhappy soul,
So asked the good sea Captain
To help her gain this goal.

He said he couldn't help her,
All who went received rebuke.
'Olivia won't see you –
She won't even see the Duke.'

Viola knew that she must work
So hatched another plan,
To be the Duke Orsino's page
By dressing as a man.

For her to put on male attire
Would be very strange indeed,
But in this place – all on her own –
It might help her to succeed.

The Captain had been kind to her
And she judged him to be fair,
She told him what she planned to do
And also made him swear

To keep her project secret,
Which he promised he would do,
And then she asked him for his help
To guide the whole plan through.

She needed some men's clothing –
He thought it very funny,
But still he said he'd help her,
And she counted out some money.

He hurried off to buy the clothes –
She told him to take care
To buy the kind of garments
That her brother used to wear.

Once dressed up in men's attire
She looked just like her brother,
It would be impossible
To tell one from the other.

And then the Captain helped her
To achieve the goal she sought
By having her presented
At the Duke Orsino's court.

She said, 'My name's Cesario.'
And so it was her plan
Had instantly succeeded
As they took her for a man.

The Duke was kind, just as she'd heard
And handsome too, forsooth;
For his part he was most impressed
With this good-looking youth.

He took Viola as his page,
Which filled her with elation,
And she did all things to fulfil
The duties of her station.

Viola was attentive
And devoted to her Lord;
She soon became his favourite,
His appreciation soared.

One day Orsino told her,
His features creased by frowns,
How he adored Olivia
Through many ups and downs.

How she refused to love him,
How she wouldn't let him call;
She wouldn't even write to him
Or communicate at all.

Viola heard his story
But it's a risky matter
To wait upon a bold young Duke
And share his idle chatter.

For she found that she now loved him
With a love that was as true
As his was for Olivia –
But, of course, he had no clue.

She let him speak – then asked him,
'If a maid loved you my Lord
But you didn't feel in any way
Of a similar accord.

'You'd tell her it was hopeless,
That your heart could not be earned,
That it was quite impossible
Her love could be returned.'

The Duke said that no lady
Could love in the same way
As he loved fair Olivia
Every moment of the day.

Viola said a woman's heart
Could equally be true;
She spoke with lively passion,
For this of course she knew.

The Duke said, 'Come, Cesario,
What know you of womankind?
How can you understand the things
That go on in their mind?'

As he spoke, poor Viola
Found she loved him even more...
But at this point a messenger
Appeared there at the door.

He'd come back from Olivia –
He'd been sent there by the Duke –
And from his face Orsino knew
He brought a fresh rebuke.

'My Lord,' the messenger began,
'I'm very much afraid
You will not like the message
Given to me by her maid.

'Her mistress will on no account
Let any see her face,
She says it shall be shrouded
By a veil of opaque lace.

'And will remain unlooked at
Till seven years go by.'
When good Orsino heard these words
He sighed a heavy sigh.

'Oh what a fine heart she must have,
Truer than any other,
That she can pay this debt of love
For her departed brother!'

He then said to Viola
'Oh, you must now depart,
Go quickly to Olivia
With the secrets of my heart.

'Insist on gaining entry.'
She said, 'And if I do,
What can I add to all the things
Olivia's heard from you?'

'Why, tell her of my passion,
And of my love,' he said,
'Tell her how strongly I desire
The two of us be wed.'

So Viola set off in haste,
Although inclined to tarry,
For now she wooed another for
The man *she* wished to marry.

She did her duty as he asked –
She could resist no-more –
And very soon she found herself
Outside Olivia's door.

She asked then for the lady,
Said she had things to tell,
The servant said her mistress
Wasn't feeling very well.

With haste Viola answered,
'What I must say won't keep.'
The servant then responded,
'But my lady's fast asleep.'

Viola was determined that
She should not call in vain,
And so she sent the servant back
To Olivia again.

At last the lady yielded
To Viola's persistence,
Which, in truth, had broken down
Olivia's resistance.

She said she'd listen once again
To Orsino's loving plea,
But warned, 'This bold new messenger
Will have no effect on me.'

Viola, entering the room,
Addressed her in this way,
'Are you the fair Olivia?
Tell me the truth, I pray.

'I would not waste my precious words
On anyone but her.'
Olivia graciously replied,
'I'm whom you seek, good sir.'

'Then please remove, I pray you,
That white, mysterious veil.'
Olivia did as she was asked –
She rather liked this male.

Pangs of desire were growing
That she could not assuage
For this young man who she believed
Was just a humble page.

Now Viola wished to get a glimpse
Of every tiny feature,
Of this sad lady whom the Duke
Thought such a lovely creature.

She knew Orsino loved her
Throughout his very being,
But Viola thought her beauty
Would lie only in the seeing.

'You are most fair,' she whispered,
'So it's little wonder why
The Duke Orsino loves you –
You're a feast for any eye.'

Olivia answered gravely,
'You are gracious and most kind,
But noble Duke Orsino
Knows all too well my mind.

'Though he is good and valiant,
This I most surely know:
I really cannot love him –
He knew that long ago.

'Tell him I cannot love him,
Tell him he must refrain,
From sending further messengers –
Unless *you* come again.'

Viola then departed
To tell what had occurred,
And when she'd gone, Olivia
Mused over every word.

She wished that this Cesario
Had been himself the Duke,
But at this thought she gave herself
A half-amused rebuke.

She cursed herself for feeling thus
But fast as this thought came
She just as fast excused herself,
As folk will do, from blame.

She ignored the gap in wealth
Between her and the page,
She forgot her strong reserve
And let her affections rage.

She wanted young Cesario
And did a reckless thing:
She told her servant, 'Follow him,
And give him this gold ring.'

The servant was told to ask
Had he left the ring behind?
Was it a present from the Duke?
If so 'twas very kind

But she could not accept it,
It was graciously returned,
Gifts of tremendous value
Should be well and truly earned.

Olivia hoped the page would see
From this discreet device
That she was now in love with him,
Not merely being nice.

Viola guessed the truth at once.
Knowing nothing of the ring,
She clearly saw how matters stood –
It was the weirdest thing.

She saw her master's lady
Was now in love with her,
It was the very strangest thing
That ever could occur.

'Alas!' poor Viola cried,
'Things are not what they seem.
The sorrowing Olivia
Has fallen for a dream.

'For my disguise has caused her sigh
These fruitless sighs for me,
As I do for Orsino
Though neither love can be.'

Returning to Orsino,
She told him of the score.
She said, 'Olivia firmly says,
Don't bother anymore.'

The Duke was still determined
That he would get his way;
He sent Cesario again
To try the following day.

Before he left the Duke desired
A love song to be sung,
And noticed that Cesario,
A gentle boy and young,

Was most affected by this song.
Its soulful, sad refrain
Of deep and unrequited love
Told of a lover's pain.

'Now on my life,' exclaimed the Duke,
'Cesario, don't be coy,
Have you beheld a face you love?
Say honestly, my boy.'

Cesario declared he had.
Then said the Duke, 'Tell me,
What sort of woman might this be?
What kind of age is she?'

So to the object of her heart
She said with deep affection,
'My Lord she is about your age
And has the same complexion.'

This made the Duke smile broadly
To find this youthful page
Should love a dark-haired woman
Who was somewhere near *his* age.

Viola returned again,
And Olivia made no fight
Because she thought the handsome page
A very welcome sight.

Viola tried, in her disguise,
Everything she could
To plead the Duke Orsino's case
But her pleading did no good.

Lady Olivia briskly said,
'I asked you to refrain,
From speaking of the noble Duke –
Don't speak of him again.

'I'd much prefer another suit.'
This was the plainest talk;
It was a road that Viola
Had little wish to walk.

Olivia spoke again at length
And opened up her mind,
She said that young Cesario
Was the dearest love she'd find.

When on Viola's handsome face
Concern began to fashion,
She saw she was the victim of
An unrequited passion.

'I see contempt upon your face
Now I have let you know,
But despite the way you feel
I truly love you so.'

But in vain the lady wooed,
Viola wished to leave,
She simply wanted to depart
And let Olivia grieve.

She said she would not come again
To plead Orsino's case,
Or ever love a woman;
Then she hurried from that place.

Viola, consumed by guilt,
Thought, 'I've been very cruel.'
But then, as she reached the street,
Was challenged to a duel.

She didn't recognise this man
Who was her persecutor,
But he had been Olivia's
One-time rejected suitor.

He was mad because he'd heard
Olivia loved a page,
The very thought had put him in
A fierce and towering rage.

What now could poor Viola do?
Fight on her own accord?
She was a mere woman,
She couldn't use a sword.

Her rival then began to shout
His sword was fully drawn.
She nearly there and then confessed
To being a woman born.

But then another stranger who
By chance was passing by
Spoke as if he were a friend,
She'd no idea why.

'If this youth has caused offence,'
He said, 'I'll take the blame,
But if you cross your sword with mine,
Take heed – 'twill be no game.'

Before she could enquire
Why he helped her in this way,
An officer stopped her new friend –
He had some words to say.

The officer had come along
To arrest him then and there,
The stranger said to Viola,
'This really isn't fair.'

And so he was arrested
For what was an old offence.
He seemed unable to provide
A reasonable defence.

And then he said to Viola,
'Return the purse I gave to you.'
She wondered what all this could mean –
She didn't have a clue.

'Why do you look surprised?' he asked.
Viola looked quite fazed;
She said she didn't know him,
His words left her amazed.

Moreover she was adamant,
She'd never had his purse.
The stranger raved on angrily
And then began to curse.

'You utter such ungrateful words
With every single breath,
Was it not I who snatched you from
The very jaws of death.'

He spoke as if he knew her,
Not like a perfect stranger.
'For you, I travelled to this place,
And now I'm in great danger.

'You have been most disloyal
To one who was a friend.'
His words came tumbling angrily,
A torrent without end.

He called her 'good Sebastian',
Then, 'Sebastian' again;
Viola tried to quiz him
But her words were all in vain.

For he was taken then in charge,
Though he shouted, cursed and raved.
Viola wondered if it was
Her twin whom he had saved.

She hoped he knew her brother,
(Which was in fact the case)
You will recall these noble twins
Bore each the self-same face.

The stranger was a sailor,
Antonio by name,
And that he'd saved Sebastian's life
Was not an idle claim.

He'd found her brother drowning,
A victim of fatigue;
So this then was the answer
To this very strange intrigue.

Once he had saved Sebastian
From the great tumultuous storm,
The friendship then between the two
Became extremely warm.

He kept Sebastian company
Wherever he would go,
And that's what caused the muddle
Of which we already know.

Sebastian had been quite keen
To see Orsino's court;
Antonio, though, was known there
For a fight that he'd once fought.

He'd wounded the Duke's nephew
So knew that without fail,
If ever he returned there
He could end up in jail.

But Antonio had decided
To take his chance and come,
Persuaded by Sebastian
Who was now his closest chum.

He'd said, upon arrival,
'Take my purse – buy what you will.
I'll wait here at the nearby inn
Until you've shopped your fill.'

But when his friend did not return
At the appointed time,
He'd left the inn ... and now had been
Arrested for his crime.

He had mistaken Viola
For Sebastian, it's true –
And that is why he'd boldly said,
'I'll fight this fight for you.'

But Viola, of course, denied
She had Antonio's purse;
She said she didn't know him –
Things went from bad to worse...

The thought of such ingratitude
Is really very bad.
No wonder that Antonio
Was mortified and mad.

Antonio was led away
And Viola then took flight;
She wouldn't give the suitor chance
To pick another fight.

But just a short time later
Sebastian came along,
The suitor thought, 'That page again!'
Of course he was quite wrong.

He went straight for Sebastian,
Struck him a hefty blow.
Sebastian was quite amazed
But didn't let it show.

He simply drew his sword to fight –
But then who should come out?
Olivia – to find out what
The noise was all about.

She called, 'My dearest love, come here,
I beg you, quickly, do!'
Then turning to the suitor snapped,
'Begone! I don't want you.'

Sebastian was most surprised
At the care she chose to show,
But he was glad thus to escape
From a foe he didn't know.

For her part fair Olivia
Was ecstatically inclined
To think that young Cesario
Had completely changed his mind.

No sign of disenchantment
Showed on his handsome face,
And of his former coolness
There was not the slightest trace.

Sebastian was quite relaxed,
And took it in good part,
He thought her strange but just supposed
She had a kindly heart.

He saw she was the mistress
Of all that he surveyed,
And when she showed she loved him – well,
His heart was quickly swayed.

She thought that her Cesario,
For such he seemed to be,
Was in a most receptive mood
So said, 'Please marry me.'

Sebastian declared he would –
A priest came right away,
And they were married there and then;
She would not brook delay.

Of course Sebastian wanted
To tell Antonio;
He said, 'I'll go and fetch him.
I can't wait to let him know.'

Sebastian then hurried off,
'I won't be long,' he said,
'Antonio won't believe me
When I tell him I am wed.'

The Duke arrived upon the scene
With Viola at his side.
An officer approached and said,
'This rogue here must be tried.'

He brought in poor Antonio,
In chains, who quickly saw
Young Viola with Orsino
Outside Olivia's door.

He thought, 'There's my Sebastian.'
And cried, now feeling glad,
'This is my friend – he'll vouch for me.'
The Duke thought he was mad.

'Three months ago,' he carried on,
'I saved this youth at sea.'
The Duke replied with great disdain,
'*Then* he was *here* with me.'

Appearing then, Olivia,
Saw Viola and said,
'Cesario, my darling!'
Viola turned bright red.

The Duke on hearing these fond words
Flew into a rage,
He said, 'Come here you wretched boy,
You most unfaithful page.'

Olivia called out after them,
'Cesario, I'm your wife.'
Viola cried, 'Not so – I love
The Duke more than my life.'

Olivia then stopped them.
'This honest priest,' she said,
'Will vouch that dear Cesario
And myself have just got wed.'

Her words cut through Orsino
With the sharpness of a knife,
He found it hard to credit that
She was his page's wife.

He realised with anguish
That his greatest love had wed,
And, turning to Cesario,
'Out of my sight!' he said.

The course that things had taken
Was just what Viola feared,
But at this point her double,
Unexpected, re-appeared.

It was her lost Sebastian
Who came upon the scene,
Whereat they all looked quite amazed –
What could this marvel mean?

The twins were truly overjoyed
To find once more each other;
He hugged his sister warmly,
She kissed her long lost brother.

So everything was now explained –
Olivia then said,
'It seems I've loved a woman
But I'll love her twin instead.'

So with Olivia now wed
All hopes of her must die.
The Duke, however, was well-known
To have a roving eye.

He thought about young Viola,
How lovely she had been;
He'd always thought 'Cesario' was
The fairest page he'd seen.

He thought how she had often shown
On many countless days
How she adored and cared for him
In many different ways.

These thoughts revolving in his mind
He soon began to see
That she was meant for him – so said,
'Cesario, marry me.'

The Duke still used the name which she
Had given at the start.
But Viola looked at him and said,
'I will with all my heart.'

Olivia, on seeing that
Their love had blossomed, said,
'Come, meet the priest right now and then
The two of you can wed.'

So it was that these siblings both
Were married in this way,
Twin brother and twin sister
Tied the knot the self-same day.

And it is true, I think, to say
Neither would have lost their heart,
If their ship had not been sunk
And they'd not been torn apart.

A feud so old and deadly
that they all were tangled in

ROMEO AND JULIET

Imagine for a moment
Two great families at war,
And no one can remember
What it is they're fighting for.

A feud so old and deadly
That they all were tangled in,
The servants and retainers
And far flung kith and kin.

Thus it was in fair Verona
Many long years ago,
Two families who'd forgotten
Why they loathed each other so.

Sometimes a youthful Capulet
And a Montague would meet
In Verona's central square,
In the market-place or street.

You should have heard the awful names
And insults each would call,
And usually the whole affair
Would end up in a brawl.

One day the old Lord Capulet
Threw a truly lavish ball,
He said, 'You're all invited,
Everybody – one and all.'

What he didn't say, of course –
There was no reason to –
Montagues weren't welcome,
As everyone there knew.

But young and handsome Romeo,
A Montague to his core,
Decided he would go
Despite the family war.

Attended by two trusted friends,
He'd set himself a task,
And to avoid detection
They each wore a fancy mask.

They took this highly dangerous risk
Right at our story's start
For no more serious reason
Than a matter of the heart.

For Romeo loved Rosaline,
A rather pretty girl;
Though friendly with the Capulets
She'd set his heart awhirl.

Benvolio and Mercutio,
His two companions, said
The girl was no great beauty,
Romeo was off his head.

If he would look at other girls
Who'd be there at the ball,
He'd find that Rosaline was not
The fairest one at all.

He'd see she was no graceful swan,
Merely an ugly crow;
So it was that Romeo
Had been induced to go.

Arriving they were greeted
In a very charming way,
By kindly old Lord Capulet
Who had these words to say.

'The ladies here are keen to dance,
Though not with me I fear.
I'm too old to trip with them
Or whisper in their ear.

'At my advanced time of life
I would never dare to ask,
Although perhaps like you young lads
I should hide behind a mask.'

They laughed and then took partners
And all began to dance,
When Romeo's wandering gaze
Fell on a lady, just by chance.

A lady whose rare beauty
Gleamed like the brightest light,
A rich and wondrous jewel
That could light the darkest night.

He said, 'I have not loved before
This moment – happy night!
Truly I have never seen
A more enchanting sight.'

He knew that she was meant for him,
In this he had no choice,
But as he whispered of his love
Someone recognised his voice.

''Tis Romeo here at our ball,'
Cried Tybalt in a passion,
'How dare he come to us tonight
And gate-crash in this fashion.'

Bold Tybalt overcome with rage,
Had flushed the brightest red,
Given the chance he would have struck
Young Romeo down dead.

Though Tybalt could not bear to see
A Montague at the ball,
His uncle, good Lord Capulet
Said he didn't mind at all.

'I've heard it said young Romeo's
A well-respected youth,
So he can stay – just for tonight –
I'm sure I heard the truth.'

Tybalt was forced into retreat
And fell back in confusion,
But he vowed that Romeo
Would pay for this intrusion.

When the dancing was over
Romeo looked for his new belle,
For he was lost forever,
A captive to her spell.

The mask was his disguise as he
Approached to where she stood,
He then took her hand in his
Though not certain if he should.

He called her hands a holy shrine
Too good for his to hold,
And now he'd dared to touch them
She must think him far too bold.

But as a blushing pilgrim
He would kiss them to atone.
Now waiting for her answer,
His whole body turned to stone.

'Good pilgrim,' said the lady,
'There is something that you miss,
For saints have hands which pilgrims touch
But which they may not kiss.'

'Saints have lips and pilgrims too,'
Romeo was quick to say.
'Ay, that is true,' the lady said,
'Lips they should use to pray.'

In this flirtatious manner
The pair spoke to each other,
Until a servant summoned her
To wait upon her mother.

It was the young girl's nurse
Who called her thus away,
So Romeo asked the servant,
'Who is that lady, pray?'

She told him, 'It is Juliet,
Who is of greatest worth,
Daughter of Lord Capulet,
Therefore of noble birth.'

So it was that Romeo
Came in this way to know,
That he'd engaged his very heart
To his family's great foe.

This made him very worried
Though his heart and mind were set,
Because he now was deep in love
With a hated Capulet.

And Juliet's love was settled
Even though she also knew
She'd fallen for an enemy,
A detested Montague.

Now as the hour was getting late
He and his friends departed,
But leaving Juliet's house so soon
Made Romeo downhearted.

So he stole back and, moving
Quite as silent as a mouse,
Climbed nimbly up the garden wall,
A short way from the house.

He landed in an orchard,
He saw a window up above.
He gazed at it and thought about
His new and truest love.

The orchard was deserted –
No guard as he had feared –
And as he stood there looking up
Sweet Juliet appeared.

Upon her balcony she stood,
An enchanting visual feast,
Her beauty radiant as the sun
As it rises in the east.

She leant her hand upon her cheek,
Sighed to the heavens above,
Romeo gazed in ecstasy,
His heart aflame with love.

Then Juliet began to speak
Thinking she could not be heard;
Romeo hiding in the dark
Heard each and every word.

Alive with youthful passion,
Her cheeks now all aglow,
She called out to the velvet night,
'Why are you "Romeo"?

'Oh, throw aside your family,
Refuse your given name;
If you will be my own true love,
I'll gladly do the same.'

On hearing this outpouring
Of the love he had awoken,
You'd think he would have shown himself,
Waved up to her or spoken.

But Romeo wished to hear much more.
He hid and heard her chide,
How he should change his surname,
How love can't be denied.

Then he cried out, 'Oh, call me "love" –
Make any name your choice.'
Juliet was most alarmed
To hear a young man's voice.

At first she was quite startled,
It gave her quite a fright,
To know he'd heard her secret
In the darkest dead of night.

And though she'd only heard him speak
A hundred words or so,
She knew the voice was surely that
Of dearest Romeo.

She said he was in danger,
He should not have come at all,
He'd put himself at dreadful risk
To scale the orchard wall.

For if the guards had caught him
They'd have surely run him through,
And for no other reason
Than he was a Montague.

'Better that they end my life,
Send me to heaven above,
Than I should waste existence here
Without fair Juliet's love.'

As he spoke a crimson flush
Spread over Juliet's face,
To cover it she quickly said,
'How came you to this place?'

'Love guided me,' he answered,
'And if you were lost to me
On some wild, far and distant shore
Washed by a pearly sea,

'I'd venture forth to seek and find
Such priceless merchandise,
The fairest that has ever come
Before my lovelorn eyes.'

Juliet wished she could retrieve
The words that she had said,
Because now he knew her heart
She blushed a deep dark red.

If only the whole evening
Could be put into reverse,
Then she could act the lady –
Frown and be perverse.

She'd summon up some coyness
So he'd value what he'd won,
But as he knew her feelings
He might think it was just fun.

For when things are too easy
It does decrease their worth,
It's always best if love can have
A long, protracted birth.

She said 'Please don't think ill of me,
This would be most unkind.
It was by chance you overheard
The thoughts within my mind.

'Perhaps I've been imprudent –
You should have made more running,
I should have been like others who
Are artful, smart and cunning.'

Romeo swore he never had
Intended to imply,
Dishonour to his lady –
He hadn't meant to spy.

He said, 'Make now, a vow of love
To me this very night.'
She said, 'How can I give it, though
You ask for it outright?

'My heart is yours already,
For I gave it when you heard
My personal confession –
I meant it, every word.'

Juliet's nurse then called her,
It was time to be abed –
'If you love me, marry me,'
Then Juliet boldly said.

He readily agreed to this,
Sweet Juliet's welcome plea,
And said with adoration,
'You're a dream come true for me.'

Romeo was loathe to part
Though it was getting light,
But in the end they bade farewell
On this auspicious night.

As he went fair Juliet said,
'Parting is such sweet sorrow,
That I will say a fond farewell
Until we meet tomorrow.'

Romeo just couldn't sleep
Because of his emotions,
So sought out Friar Lawrence who
Was then at his devotions.

And when he saw young Romeo
In the early morning light,
The holy man was quick to guess
He'd not been home that night.

He thought that love for Rosaline
At first, had kept him out,
But Romeo soon told him
What his visit was about.

'A passion for sweet Juliet
Has swept my heart away;
I've come to ask, dear Friar,
Will you marry us today?'

The Friar knew that Rosaline
Had caused the lad much pain,
How she had just ignored him
And viewed him with disdain.

But now he loved another girl,
To judge from his deep sighs.
He said, 'Men's love is fickle,
They love only with their eyes.'

But the Friar thought the match
Could really be good news:
It might heal the rift between
Capulets and Montagues.

He was friend to both of them
And fond of Romeo,
Here was a chance at last to heal
This wretched tale of woe.

So he readily agreed.
'Of course I will,' he said,
'It would be truly excellent
If the two of you got wed.'

A messenger was sent at once:
'Fetch Juliet as well!'
And happily she made her way
To the humble Friar's cell.

They exchanged their solemn vows –
The marriage was a fact –
The Friar prayed to heaven
To smile kindly on this act.

Then Juliet hurried homewards,
Though she didn't want to go,
To wait until the night should come
And her dear Romeo.

Mercutio and Benvolio
Later that day were walking,
Through Verona's pretty streets
And they were quietly talking...

Then some Capulets appeared
With Tybalt at their head;
Tybalt who'd been at the ball,
And this is what he said.

'Mercutio, you are a friend
Of Romeo, that cur.'
To which Mercutio replied,
'What's that to you, good sir?'

At once an argument broke out
With the makings of a fray,
When Romeo encountered them.
By chance, he passed that way.

When Tybalt beheld Romeo
He soon began to curse,
He called him cur and villain
And things that were much worse.

Romeo did not intend
To fight him or be rude,
He'd never taken any part
In the family's old feud.

And Tybalt as we know was one
Of Juliet's closest kin,
He didn't want to fight him
Though he knew that he would win.

He called him 'Honest Capulet',
To show he liked him well,
But Tybalt hated Montagues
In the way he hated hell.

He'd not hear any reason
And drew out his sword to fight,
Mercutio was enraged to see
This most aggressive sight.

He simply couldn't understand
How Romeo stayed so calm,
Then all at once two swords engaged
To everyone's alarm.

Mercutio fought Tybalt
Spurred by the words they'd said,
When from a sudden, fatal thrust
Mercutio dropped down dead.

Romeo lost his temper
On seeing his dead friend,
He raised his sword to fight Tybalt
Right to the bitter end.

They fought until the moment
When Tybalt cried in pain,
And dropping to the blood-stained ground
Was well and truly slain.

It was just before midday
So the message quickly spread,
Mercutio and Tybalt
Lay in the street, stone dead.

Capulets and Montagues
Arrived from where they'd been;
And the Prince of fair Verona
Was quickly at the scene.

He ordered good Benvolio
To recount what had occurred,
And as he spoke the gathered throng
Hung on his every word.

Benvolio spoke boldly
Though he was badly shaken;
He tried to justify the part
That Romeo had taken.

The grief of Lady Capulet
For Tybalt knew no end;
She said, 'Benvolio's lying
For he is Romeo's friend.'

She begged to be revenged
For the deed that they all saw –
She didn't know she pleaded
Against her son-in-law.

Lord Montague was also there
Accompanying his wife,
This lady pleaded fervently
For her son Romeo's life.

'Tybalt slew Mercutio.'
She said it was *his* fault.
So they argued back and forth
Until the Prince called, 'Halt!'

He was unmoved by pleadings,
By passionate shouts and cries,
The time had come for judgement,
A time to be most wise.

He said: 'I banish Romeo,
The punishment is set.'
This would be grievous news indeed
For his new bride, Juliet.

When she heard she raged against
Her Romeo with force,
After their recent marriage
These were grounds for a divorce.

She raged for killing Tybalt,
It was such a wicked sin,
Tybalt was, as we well know,
One of her dearest kin.

Romeo was a 'fiend from hell',
A 'wolf', a 'deadly dove',
But when her rage grew calmer,
She could not deny her love.

The tears she shed for Tybalt
In all her fearful grief,
Were mingled with a hundred tears
Of gladness and relief

That Romeo was still alive
Whom Tybalt would have slain;
She thought then of his exile
And the tears welled up again.

Romeo sought refuge now
In Friar Lawrence's cell,
No surprise, he didn't take
His sentence very well.

He cried, 'I never wanted
To have that stupid fight,
There is no way that I can live
If not in Juliet's sight.

'For paradise is where she is,
The whole thing is unfair.'
Wild and mad and frantic,
He vainly tore his hair.

The gentle Friar calmed him down,
Encouraged him to seek,
The strength to overcome his woes
And not be quite so weak.

For after all, things could be worse:
Did he not still have life,
And Juliet still loved him
And she was still his wife.

'Take leave,' the kindly Friar said
'Of your Juliet tonight,
Then hasten to Mantua
And there keep out of sight.

'When time is right I will announce
To everyone you know,
How Juliet is married
To the banished Romeo.

'Montagues and Capulets
Should now behave as one,
The first have a new daughter
And the others a new son.

'Then the Prince will surely come
To feel – all in good time –
The union is for the best
And pardon you your crime.

'So hurry now to Juliet,
And you will feel much better,
Then get you gone to Mantua –
I'll send all news by letter.'

And so the pair enjoyed that night
Alone in wedded pleasure;
Their happiness was far beyond
All normal rules of measure.

But neither could forget the fact
That Romeo was departing,
Just at the very moment
When their marriage should be starting.

A few short days had barely passed
Since Romeo had left,
When Juliet was feeling sad,
Borne down and quite bereft.

And then Lord Capulet outlined
A little plan he'd hatched:
He proposed that Juliet
And Count Paris should be matched.

He was an ideal suitor,
Gallant, noble, steady;
He'd have made a perfect spouse
Were she not wed already.

Juliet was terrified
But how could she explain?
Knowing she was wed would cause
Her father too much pain.

And so she made excuses
And used almost any ploy,
She said, 'How could I marry
With any sense of joy?

'I grieve for poor, dead Tybalt,
My day is turned to night,
To marry at a time like this
Would not be seen as right.

'Besides, I am too young, it is
Too early in my life.'
Of course she daren't reveal the fact
That she was Romeo's wife.

But all her words were wasted,
The Lord was not amused,
He said he was determined
And she could not be excused.

He told her to make ready
And then added, 'This I warn,
You will marry the Count Paris
On this coming Thursday morn.

'And if you should oppose me
I'll disown you as my kin.'
Juliet was nearly mad
At the pickle she was in.

She went to Friar Lawrence
In a state of great distress –
She always went to see him
When her life was in a mess.

She said, 'I'll not wed Paris
Despite my father's warning,
I'd rather die than marry him
Thursday, or *any* morning.'

The Friar said, 'Go home my dear,
Say you will mend your way,
Consent to your good father
For this coming wedding day.

'The night before the wedding
When you're on your own awhile,
In solitude and silence
Drink the contents of this phial.

'Then for two and forty hours,'
The Friar softly said,
'Your body will seem lifeless,
And cold as though you're dead.

'They'll take you to the family vault,
Laid on a funeral bier,
Although it may seem frightening,
There is nothing there to fear.

'Once you're there, I promise
There will be no mistake,
After two and forty hours
You will suddenly awake.

'I'll make sure that Romeo
Is there when you come round,
To take you to Mantua.
Now how does that all sound?'

The dread of wedding Paris
Made her accept this trial,
She promised she would swallow
All the contents of the phial.

As Juliet left the Friar
Paris came up to her side,
So, modestly dissembling,
She agreed to be his bride.

When Lord Capulet heard of this,
How she had changed her mind,
His manner once again became
Supremely bright and kind.

He said, 'It will be perfect!
Best day Verona's seen!'
Her father never said a word
He didn't really mean.

Our story moves on quickly
With sad, relentless motion;
The night before her wedding
Juliet drank the potion.

She thought of her dear Romeo
And in a whisper said,
'I'll drink it now' – and did so,
Then fell – as if stone dead.

When Paris came next morning
To start his wedded life,
He found his lovely bride to be
Could never be his wife.

She lay quite still and ghostly pale,
Appearing to be dead;
He felt that he had lost a wife,
Although they'd never wed.

But even more distressing
As that sad day was dawning,
Were Juliet's poor parents
Now heavily in mourning.

They had lost their only child,
'Oh tragedy!' they said,
'There will be no wedding now,
Our lovely daughter's dead.'

Juliet lay on the bier,
A dismal wedding bed,
She was placed within the vault,
The living with the dead.

Bad news can travel faster
Than good – as you will know,
And so the news of Juliet's death
Soon reached Romeo.

A message from the Friar
To inform him all was well,
Did not get to Romeo
And why we cannot tell.

Romeo was drowning
In a deep depressing gloom,
Half-mad with grief he *had* to see
His wife within her tomb.

He bought himself some poison
With which to end his life;
He was intent on dying
And then lying with his wife.

He hurried to Verona
And after a frantic search,
He found beloved Juliet's tomb
Beside a little church.

He prized the tomb wide open,
He was desperate to break through
When a voice cried from the darkness
'Desist, vile Montague.'

It was Count Paris guarding
The sham of his wedding bed,
He knew not why young Romeo
Should have interest in the dead.

He only knew he was a foe,
A Montague – that name! –
Stealing here in dead of night
To do some deed of shame.

Romeo bade Paris go,
'Leave me here, I pray.
If you provoke my anger,
You will with Tybalt lay.'

But Paris wouldn't listen,
He knew it wasn't right
That a banished man should be here,
Alone at dead of night.

So he attacked and their swords
Clashed time and time again,
A deft thrust from Romeo
Left poor Count Paris slain.

Romeo ran into the tomb
And saw Juliet asleep,
The sight of her just lying there
Made him break down and weep.

He saw the shrouded Tybalt
And to the corpse he said,
'Your soul can rest in peace, my friend,
I too will soon be dead.'

Romeo kissed Juliet
Then without the slightest sound,
He drank the poisonous potion
And collapsed upon the ground.

If only he had waited
If only he'd not taken
The poison at the moment
Juliet would awaken.

Now came the hour for the Friar
To set fair Juliet free,
As he drew closer to the vault
He was horrified to see,

Paris lying in his blood,
A grim, depressing sight.
And then he saw within the tomb
A dimly, burning light.

As the Friar went in to see
What rare sequence of chance
Had caused these strange and fearful things...
Juliet woke from her trance.

When she opened up her eyes
She saw his friendly face,
Then remembered where she was –
That cold, horrific place.

As she came to she asked the priest,
'Where is my Romeo?'
The Friar in a panic cried,
'Quick now – for we must go.'

The Friar hurried from the tomb
As Juliet looked around,
And then she saw that Romeo
Lay dead upon the ground.

She saw the cup of poison
And soft tears welled in her eyes,
She knew that this had been the cause
Of her Romeo's demise.

Her agony was boundless,
She was totally bereft,
She grabbed the cup of poison –
There was no poison left.

Now her Romeo was dead
There was nothing to live for,
So hearing people coming,
She drew the knife he wore.

She stabbed herself with its sharp blade
And instantly she died –
And that is how they found her,
Lying dead by Romeo's side.

The Count's page had seen the fight
And quickly raised the alarm,
Up and down the streets he ran
And broke the people's calm.

He shouted out the lover's names
And called out 'Something's wrong.'
He woke up all Verona
As he made his way along.

The Prince and old Lord Capulet,
Lord Montague as well,
Roused themselves from cosy beds
To hear what he might tell.

The Friar was apprehended
And joined the motley throng,
The great Prince then demanded,
'What in the world is wrong?'

And then within the hearing
Of everybody there
The grieving Friar told the part
He'd played in this affair.

Informing both the families
Of everything he knew,
Of how the tragic, star-crossed pair
Were in love and married too.

How he had hoped their marriage
Which had joined them both by law,
Would reconcile their families
And stop the age-old war.

The Prince turned to both fathers,
'My Lords,' he said, 'take heed,
See how the wrath of heaven
Has caused your hearts to bleed.

'A true love for each other
Has brought about their fate,
Their loss is now your punishment
For your deep and selfish hate.

'This surely must exceed the worst
The pair of you can stand.'
Lord Capulet then quietly asked
His foe to take his hand.

They embraced with many tears,
Their hate disappeared in waves,
And they agreed to bury war
In their children's early graves.

And so amid this tragic scene
Our sorry story ends,
And Montagues and Capulets
Became the best of friends.

And all agree there's never been
A story of more woe
Than this of noble Juliet
And her dear Romeo.

He seized upon a pillow

OTHELLO, THE MOOR OF VENICE

This is a tale where murder,
Lying, envy and deceit,
Burning love and jealousy,
In tragedy all meet.

Our story starts in Venice,
This is where our scene is set
Where a beautiful young maiden
And a soldier have just met.

Her name is Desdemona
And her feelings are all bent
On this high-ranking general
Who's of Moorish descent.

The man is called Othello,
He's experienced in war,
Venetians loved him dearly
And called him just 'The Moor'.

He'd talk to Desdemona
And tell her all he'd done,
He'd make his great adventures
Appear like harmless fun.

She would listen open mouthed
As all his tales unravelled
About exciting places
To which he'd boldly travelled.

He'd tell her of past battles,
Of fights that he had fought,
Of daring escapades, and how
Sometimes he had been caught.

As Desdemona listened
So her love was born and grew;
Othello soon discovered
He was falling for her too.

The lady was of noble birth
And so she was quite sure
Her father would be angry
If he knew she loved the Moor.

But she adored him truly
And she found she couldn't hide
Her feelings for Othello,
They could not be denied.

So when he spoke of his great love
And boldly said to her,
'Desdemona, marry me!'
She was eager to concur.

Brabantio, her father,
Would not willingly agree,
And if she told him of her plan
He'd be furious as could be.

He had wanted her to wed
A Venetian nobleman;
It was his expectation,
This had always been his plan.

And so they married secretly
But knew 'twould not be long
Before Brabantio found out,
And here they were not wrong.

'Othello has used witchcraft
And devious spells,' he said,
'To steal my daughter from me
And make her lose her head.'

Complaining to the senate,
He told them, 'This Othello,
May be a marvellous general
But he's a wicked fellow.'

If times had been less turbulent
His case might have been heard
But the senate was intent upon
Events that had occurred.

A mighty fleet had just set sail
From a distant Turkish quay
And set a course for Cyprus
Out across the open sea.

Now Venice governed Cyprus
And the state had cause to fear
That the Turks would raid the island,
And their fleet was drawing near.

And so the senate had to choose
Someone to save the isle;
They put it to the vote –
Othello won it by a mile.

They summoned brave Othello,
But when the great Moor came
Brabantio flew at him
Crying, 'What's your cunning game?

'You have bewitched my daughter,
You've made her lose all sense.'
Othello then responded
With a quiet eloquence.

He said, 'I love your daughter,
The only craft I used
Was my sincere affection;
I'm not guilty as accused.'

The lovely Desdemona then
Appeared before the door.
She cried out to her father,
'I'm in love with this brave Moor.

'He has become my husband,
You must accept it's so.'
Brabantio saw clearly
That he had nowhere to go.

He saw that he had little choice:
Agree or just withdraw;
So called Othello to him
And embraced the noble Moor.

Once reconciled Othello found
That he had much to do.
He headed off for Cyprus
And his new wife went there too.

While sailing to the island
The Moor prepared to meet
The large, impressive army
Coming with the Turkish fleet.

Then he received good news, that all
Their ships had disappeared.
A sudden storm had blown away
The fleet they had so feared.

It had dispersed the enemy,
Things did not look so black;
Othello felt quite certain
They were safe now from attack.

But as he was rejoicing
At this unlooked-for win,
He did not know that very soon
His problems would begin.

Othello had a dear friend,
Most charming in his way;
The ladies loved to listen
To the things he had to say.

Handsome and engaging,
Everybody loved him so,
This popular young soldier
Was called Michael Cassio.

Now he had served Othello
In a hundred different ways,
And helped win Desdemona
In Othello's courting days.

He'd tell young Desdemona
How Othello would despair,
If she refused to love him,
Or he thought she didn't care.

So Desdemona soon became
Quite close to Cassio;
Othello didn't mind a bit –
He knew she loved him so.

And after they were married
Michael Cassio still found
He'd get the warmest welcome
Any time he went around.

Othello wasn't wary – felt
No jealousy at all;
Extending a warm welcome
When Cassio came to call.

He took things at face value,
He trusted wife and friend,
He never would have credited
How everything would end.

Othello had promoted
Young Cassio to the post
Of second-in-command
Because he trusted him the most.

There was another officer –
Iago was his name –
Who felt his right to hold this post
The more deserving claim.

So now he hated Cassio
And hatched an evil plan
That would persuade Othello
He had chosen the wrong man.

He criticised his rival,
His words had a truthful ring;
But Othello took no notice
And he didn't change a thing.

So Iago's hatred turned upon
Othello now as well –
First, for not promoting him
And second, we must tell,

Othello had become quite close
To Iago's kindly wife,
So Iago was now scheming
To wreck Othello's life.

He formed a devious plan that would
Wreak havoc, he was sure,
Upon fair Desdemona,
And on Cassio and the Moor.

Now cunning Iago was well-versed
In the ways of human kind;
He knew the direst torments were
Those that affect the mind.

He thought, 'I'll make the Moor believe
His wife has been untrue,
That she's in love with Cassio
And that he loves her too.'

And so when brave Othello
And his great fleet reached the isle
Iago came out to meet him
With a broad, but two-faced, smile.

Othello said, 'I see all's well.'
Then, stepping on the shore,
'Let's have a celebration
Now there's no more threat of war.'

While everyone made merry,
Though it seemed a little hard,
Othello sent young Cassio
To mind the castle guard.

Othello told the officer,
'The soldiers must behave,
Don't let them have strong drink at all
No matter how they crave.'

But then as Cassio mounted guard
Iago, full of charm,
Said, 'Have a little drink, good sir.
One drink can't do you harm.'

At first good Cassio declined,
And stubbornly resisted,
Until at last he acquiesced,
For Iago had persisted.

And then it didn't take too long
Before it came to pass
That Cassio was drinking
Each and every proffered glass.

And so it was he got quite drunk
And belligerent too;
Then he got into a fight –
As drunks will often do.

When Othello came along
His face began to frown,
He saw at once that discipline
Had badly broken down.

So he demoted Cassio
And withdrew his senior rôle,
Thus Iago, at a stroke, achieved
The first part of his goal.

Cassio did not recall
That Iago'd got him drunk;
His only recollection
Was of shame at how he'd sunk.

So as he thought that Iago
Was still his friend, he said,
'Whatever made me get so drunk?
I must have lost my head.

'And now Othello hates me,
Judging by his looks.
Will you tell me how can I
Get back in his good books?'

Iago replied, 'There is a way,
There's one thing you can do,
Get to Othello through his wife,
I'm sure that she'll help you.'

So Cassio, as Iago planned
Approached Othello's wife.
He said, 'I've been demoted,
I've messed up my whole life.

'Oh, please speak to your husband,
Ask him to pardon me.'
She said, 'My friend, of course I will,
I'm sure that we'll soon see

'Othello will forgive you.
I'll go and plead your case
And get you reinstated
To your former, rightful place.'

When Othello heard her pleas
He said, 'I keep reliving
The sight of Cassio so drunk –
It's too soon for forgiving.'

Desdemona tried once more –
Her efforts were in vain –
Then she begged him one more time
And pleaded yet again.

Her husband finally agreed,
He would forgive his crime,
But she was not to tell him,
He would – all in good time.

Iago, meanwhile put in place
The next part of his plan
By sowing vile, suspicious thoughts,
As only scoundrels can.

He asked Othello slyly
As he, pondering, bit his lip,
'What is the basis of your wife's
Very warm relationship

'With Cassio, our companion;
They seem to be so close?'
Othello looked down glumly,
His features were morose.

The subtle seeds of jealousy
Were starting to take root,
And Iago's evil scheming
Was beginning to bear fruit.

'I know my wife loves dancing
And to be in company
But I'm sure that I can trust her,
She would never cheat on me.'

Then Iago said with artful smile
'I'm sure she's not untrue
But I'd watch her carefully,
All the same if I were you.

'For she deceived her father
So she could marry you;
I should observe her closely –
She might deceive you too.'

So from that moment onward
Othello could not find
A moment of true happiness
Or any peace of mind.

Then Iago left him saying,
'Don't forgive young Cassio yet.'
And warned him to look out when next
His wife and Cassio met.

And then a little later
Iago whispered to the Moor,
'I want to speak of something
That I'm certain I just saw.

'When Cassio was walking by
I saw him wipe his face
Upon a scarlet handkerchief,
All trimmed with finest lace.'

Othello looked up startled,
For this cut him like a knife,
'That was the first love token
I ever gave my wife.

'I'll make them pay for this deceit
If all is as you say –
Yes, I will be revenged at once,
I'll deal with it today.'

Othello should have ascertained
If all he'd heard was true,
But rashly he decided
In a moment what to do.

Believing what he had been told –
Although a pack of lies –
He now behaved as if he'd seen
Her guilt with his own eyes.

The truth of the affair was this:
Sly Iago'd sent his spouse
To make a friendly visit to
Fair Desdemona's house.

And there to steal the handkerchief.
He'd said, 'I think it's nice,
I'd like a copy woven
And it has to be precise.'

His trusting wife believed him,
She said, 'I'll do my best.'
And she fulfilled successfully
Her husband's odd request.

And Iago then had dropped it
Right in poor Cassio's way,
And that is how he'd picked it up
That very fateful day.

Now when Othello met his wife
He said, 'May I impose,
And use your scarlet handkerchief?
I have a runny nose.

'I'm sure if I can use it,
It will give me some relief.'
She said, 'I cannot find it,
It's been taken by a thief.'

He asked for it once more and then,
Engulfed in awful gloom,
When his wife could not locate it,
Rushed in anger from the room.

'She's given away my present
To her lover,' he then said.
And thoughts of bloody murder surged
Through poor Othello's head.

When he returned much later
She was very quick to see
That he was mad – he said, 'You've been
A faithless wife to me.'

He wept great tears and shouted out,
'I could have borne all pain,
Except for this foul torment
That's fermenting in my brain.

'Your blatant infidelity
Has torn me right apart,
Knowing that you love another
Truly breaks my heart.'

Then he left her all alone;
Poor Desdemona cried,
How could he think she was untrue?
She'd never ever lied.

She lay there in her bedroom
With a broken heart and wept,
Then fell into a slumber,
Crying softly as she slept.

Later on the Moor came back,
He shook with every breath,
For he had now determined
To put his wife to death.

The girl would pay an awful price
For telling him a lie,
The Moor was firm in his resolve
That Desdemona die.

She should not live to play her games
With more men in her life.
He leant across the bed and kissed
His doomed and wretched wife.

He kissed her for the last time
And the touch was, oh, so sweet,
He wept as waves of tender love
Caused his great heart to beat.

Then Desdemona woke and saw
Her husband standing by,
He looked at her and softly said,
'You must prepare to die.'

She lay there at his mercy,
She begged him for compassion;
Othello trembled violently
With overpowering passion.

She begged him to inform her
Of what she had done wrong,
She swore that she'd been faithful
To their marriage all along.

He breathed the name of Cassio,
And said, 'You've been untrue.'
She answered, 'It is all a lie,
Othello – I love you.'

But he seized upon a pillow
And placed it o'er her head,
He held it firmly till he knew
That she was truly dead.

Othello drew back trembling,
Then heard knocking from outside,
It was Iago's wife who'd come,
'Can I speak to you?' she cried.

Eventually he let her in,
She'd come to let him know
That someone had just then attacked
Young Michael Cassio.

She saw sweet Desdemona
Lying dead across the bed,
She turned ghostly white with horror,
'Who did this foul thing?' she said.

Othello said he'd killed her
And he gave his reason why,
'She's been seeing Cassio,
So she deserved to die.'

He said, 'Your husband, Iago,
Said my wife had been untrue.'
She cried, 'My evil husband
Has been telling lies to you.'

Then at that very moment
Iago and some men arrived
With the wounded Cassio
Who happily had survived.

Iago's wife then told them
How she'd been asked to act the thief,
How she'd been sent to steal
Desdemona's handkerchief.

'My husband made me do it
And now Desdemona's dead,
I didn't have an inkling
It would end like this,' she said.

Othello now saw Iago's guilt
Reflected in his eyes,
He saw how he'd been taken in
By Iago's scheming lies.

Iago was very angry
To be turned on by his wife,
To stop her accusations
He stabbed her with his knife.

She died firmly insisting
That Othello's wife was chaste,
She said, 'Regret at leisure
Your deed carried out in haste.'

Her dying words cleared Cassio
And Desdemona too
So Othello realised
What his wife had said was true.

Innocent and pure as snow,
She had been all along,
Othello saw with horror
He'd committed a great wrong.

He knew his life was empty
All alone without her,
He lost the will to carry on
Now he saw the way things were.

So he pulled out his dagger
Plunged the blade into his side,
And he collapsed beside his wife
And it was there he died.

And thus Othello killed himself
In this untimely fashion,
A victim of malicious lies
And his unbending passion.

Later it was discovered
That a part of Iago's plan
Was to murder Cassio,
It was he who'd sent the man.

They seized the villain Iago
And said the price he'd pay
Was death – and it was carried out
Upon that very day.

Word travelled back to Venice
That Othello was now dead
And Desdemona also
And then everybody said,

It was a melancholy day,
And such a heavy blow
To lose fair Desdemona
And Othello in one go.

Alone, but for his jester,
King Lear's royal fool

KING LEAR

In ages past this land was ruled
By a monarch called King Lear,
Who grew sullen and depressed
As old age and death drew near.

He'd sit upon his throne for hours
And contemplate his doom;
He could bring an atmosphere
Into any happy room.

He was weary of it all,
He'd really had enough;
Ruling all of Britain
Was extremely heavy stuff.

The country needed people
With fresh, exciting vision,
So, after thinking deeply
He came to a decision.

He summoned his three daughters
And then set a little test
To find out which of all of them
Loved their old father best.

Goneril, the eldest girl,
Knelt to the king and spoke.
She knew just what he wanted,
So she really went for broke.

She said she loved him dearly,
Was his most faithful girl,
The way she went so overboard
Made your toes all want to curl.

She said he meant far more to her
Than life and liberty.
'You are my very world,' she said.
'You're everything to me.'

The king was very satisfied
He lapped up every word,
He thought her speech the nicest
His old ears had ever heard.

But she was really insincere
When she told him, 'I love you.'
She was lying through her teeth
As none of it was true.

The king, alas, was blind to this,
Believing what she said,
And blurted out the first dumb thing
That popped into his head.

'I give you and your husband
A third of my lands,' he said.
'You can have the lands right now,
Although I'm not yet dead.'

Then he called his second child
To sit down by his side,
And she behaved the self-same way –
She sat right down and lied.

The second daughter, Regan,
Was quite as bad as the first,
In fact it was impossible
To say which of them was worst.

She said that all the joys of life
Were nothing when compared
With all the love and happiness
The king and she had shared.

Poor King Lear was overcome
When he heard his daughter tell
How very much she loved him –
He gave her a third as well.

Then turning to the youngest –
Cordelia was her name –
He waited all expectantly
To hear more of the same.

For she had been his favourite
Since the day that she was born,
She'd held a special place within
His heart since that first dawn.

But Cordelia knew quite well
Her sisters weren't sincere,
She knew that they had no regard
For the king she held so dear.

She saw what they were up to,
Saw through their little game,
And as she had a heart most true
She couldn't do the same.

Their over flowery speeches
And their flattery and guile
Made poor Cordelia quite depressed
And took away her smile.

So when she spoke to the king
She replied, 'I must confess
I love you out of duty,
Nothing more and nothing less.'

The king was shaken and annoyed
How could she be so rude;
How could his favourite daughter
Show such gross ingratitude?

He said, 'You should consider
What you say with special care,
For if you don't you may find out
You'll end up with no share.'

She said, 'I can't make speeches
As my older sisters do.
How can they profess to give
All of their love to you?

'For they are married ladies
Yet say all their love is yours.
This ignores the rules of love,
Defies all Nature's laws.

'For I tell you honestly,
If I marry,' she said,
'You will keep half of my love,
Half goes to whom I wed.'

Cordelia really loved the king,
Her sisters *claimed* they did;
She'd always doted on him
Ever since she was a kid.

And so now she understated,
Maybe with words too plain.
She didn't want him thinking
She was merely out for gain.

Old King Lear saw none of this,
He cried, 'You shall not get
An acre of my kingdom now.'
He really was upset.

And so he gave Cordelia's share
To the sisters who had lied,
He didn't have an inkling
He'd been taken for a ride.

He made some small conditions
For bestowing everything:
They could have the lands and power
But he'd still be 'the king'.

And he'd retain a hundred knights
To attend on him each day,
And every other month
He'd arrange to come and stay.

He'd alternate his visits
Between his loving girls;
Unlike his youngest daughter
These two seemed like priceless pearls.

So old King Lear gave away
His kingdom in this fashion,
Action based not on good sense
But on an old man's passion.

His courtiers were astounded
And wondered what this meant.
Just one person voiced his thoughts –
This was the Earl of Kent.

He counselled, 'If you abdicate,
This action you'll regret.'
The king replied, 'Hold your tongue!
My heart and mind are set.'

Kent persisted with his pleas,
He said the king should rule.
King Lear got extremely mad,
He really lost his cool.

He said, 'Earl Kent, I banish you
Forever from my shore,
You've only got five days to leave,
And not a moment more.

'If you're still here upon the sixth
You'll breathe your final breath –
I'll have you thrown in jail and then
I'll have you put to death.'

The Earl of Kent said his farewells,
It would mean death to stay.
He bowed to young Cordelia
And then hurried on his way.

The King of France then entered,
The Duke of Burgundy too,
They pursued a common aim,
For they were there to woo.

They'd courted fair Cordelia,
They'd said they loved her so,
But now she'd lost her fortune
Would they choose to stay or go?

Burgundy soon changed his mind;
The King of France did not,
He said, 'I still will have her
As I care for her a lot.'

And so Cordelia became,
By luck and happy chance,
The bold French king's fiancée,
His intended Queen of France.

He loved her for her real worth,
And not just for her looks –
But what a thing to happen,
What a turn up for the books!

And so with mixed emotions
And with tears in her eyes
Cordelia went around the court
And made her last goodbyes.

She said to her two sisters,
'Care for father, both of you.'
They turned and angrily replied,
'Don't tell us what to do.'

And so Cordelia left them,
Going with the King of France;
And once she'd gone the sisters
Led King Lear a merry dance.

Very soon their promises
All vanished into air –
Once they'd taken all he had
They clearly didn't care.

During that first month he stayed
With Goneril as arranged;
King Lear however soon found out
Her love for him had changed.

She loathed him being in her home
With his one hundred knights,
She'd hardly speak to him at all
And they had many fights.

She treated him with great disdain;
Her servants did so too.
They paid no heed to his requests
And said, 'We shan't help you.'

But there was help at hand although
King Lear didn't know –
The brave and noble Earl of Kent
Decided not to go.

He was loyal to the king
And would be to the end,
As he clearly saw that Lear
Would need a trusty friend.

The Earl of Kent disguised himself,
His identity to hide,
He dressed up as a servant,
Laying his true self aside.

Then he applied to old King Lear
And asked him for some work,
He said, 'I will be loyal, sir,
Toil hard and never shirk.'

King Lear replied he'd take him on,
He told him, 'You're in luck,
I need someone to help me out.'
And so a deal was struck.

Though if the king had ever learned
The person he'd engaged
Was the banished Earl of Kent
He would have been enraged.

Kent gave his name as Caius
And he made it very clear
That he would do just anything
To help the great King Lear.

And so when Goneril's servants
Wouldn't do some little thing,
He'd trip them up or kick them
For insulting the old king.

And in this way he soon became
Indispensable to Lear,
The old man grew to value him
And hold him very dear.

But matters soon got even worse
Between Lear and Goneril,
She asked him, 'Why is it you need
Those knights around you still?

'They fill the court with all their noise,
They're a nuisance – that's for sure.
I really cannot understand
Why you need them anymore.'

Lear could not believe his ears,
He frowned a puzzled frown –
How could his daughter be like this
When he'd given her a crown.

He said she was ungrateful,
(Who could say he wasn't right?)
He really let her have it;
He was ready for a fight.

Goneril stuck to her guns.
She said, 'Your knights are rough.'
Lear replied, 'That's just not true.'
Then said, 'I've had enough.

'I won't be staying anymore,
You shan't treat me this way.
I'll go and stay with Regan,
And I'll go to her today.'

He told his knights, 'Prepare to leave,
We're going right away.'
Then turning to his daughter
He had these words to say.

'Oh, wretched girl, I hope if you
Have children of your own
They give you more respect and love
Than my three girls have shown.'

King Lear got really angry –
His eyes flashed, he looked wild –
For he was quite dumbfounded
By his disrespectful child.

'A thankless child is sharper
Than a serpent's tooth,' he said,
And then he shuffled out the door
With bent and heavy head.

Goneril's husband now spoke out
As Lear climbed on his horse,
He said he'd never wanted things
To take this sorry course.

King Lear replied, 'I would have thought,
Being king and at my age,
I'd have been treated better.'
He was really in a rage.

He turned his horse to leave and then
Sent Caius on ahead.
'Inform my daughter, Regan,
That I'm on my way,' he said.

Earl Kent, now known as Caius,
Galloped off in his disguise.
He reached Regan's place to find
She'd been led astray by lies.

They had come from Goneril,
Who'd sent her steward to say
King Lear was misbehaving
In the most atrocious way.

The steward there had stirred things up,
His words were very plain;
He'd told Regan that her Dad
Was now a downright pain.

Now Caius knew this steward
And he guessed what he had done,
For he was only too aware
Of the lies the rogue had spun.

And so he challenged him to fight –
The steward said, 'No fear.'
But Caius still attacked him,
And he thumped him on the ear.

When Regan heard about it
She was mad as she could be,
And she locked Caius in the stocks,
Then threw away the key.

Though Caius remonstrated
Saying, 'I've come from the king.'
Regan said she didn't care,
That didn't mean a thing.

When King Lear arrived he saw
His servant in the stocks;
This was just another link
In a chain of heavy knocks.

And things did not get better
When a servant came to say
That Regan wouldn't see him
Until the following day.

Lear insisted she be called
As he grew angrier still,
But when finally she arrived
She came with Goneril.

Regan told him to return
To Goneril's again
And send away half of the knights
Who served him in his train.

'Say sorry now to Goneril
And ask her to forgive.'
The king said, 'No, I won't do that,
However long I live.'

Now both his daughters had a go,
They told him what they thought,
And though poor King Lear argued back
His efforts came to nought.

The daughters then asked sourly,
'Why keep those knights at all?
It's quite unnecessary
To have this crowd on call.

'For you can use our servants,
You do not need your own;
Just fire the useless lot of them –
You'll get on fine alone.'

The king replied, 'If I do that,
One thing I surely know:
I go from king to beggar,
And I do it in one go.'

He could see that his cruel daughters
Were set to drive him down.
To think he'd once ruled thousands
And worn the British crown.

He vowed to be revenged on them,
But what could King Lear do?
He was a man of eighty –
And a weak and frail one too.

One thing there was for certain,
Of one fact he was quite sure –
He would not ask for shelter
At either daughter's door.

He called then for his horse and said,
'You won't see me again.'
But as he spoke a storm broke out
With thunder, wind and rain.

Despite the storm he galloped off,
His daughters didn't care.
They said that wilful men like that
Should watch out and beware.

They simply shut the door on him.
The winds and storm increased –
It seemed the might of heaven
Had in fury been released.

King Lear reached a barren heath,
With scarce a bush about.
The future did not look too good,
Of this he had no doubt.

Alone but for his jester,
King Lear's royal Fool,
He bitterly reflected on
The time he used to rule.

The king waved his fists wildly
Defying the winds to blow;
Aimlessly he stumbled on
Not knowing where to go.

He cursed the earth and heavens
For the awful storm they'd sent,
Then turning round he noticed
Our good friend, the Earl of Kent.

He saw his servant Caius –
He still didn't know his friend.
The Earl was sad to see the king
Brought to this sorry end.

The king cried out to Caius,
'Although this storm's a bind,
It's nothing when compared to that
Which rages in my mind.'

He spoke about his children
And of all the grief he'd known,
He cursed their greed and selfishness,
The ingratitude they'd shown.

As Caius looked upon the king
His tears came in a rush;
He saw his monarch was a force
Quite spent – a busted flush.

Caius begged the king to shelter,
There was a hut close by.
'If you shelter there,' he said,
'There's a chance you may get dry.'

It was standing on its own,
A bleak, depressing place.
The fool, who went in first, ran out
With fear upon his face.

He cried, 'There is a ghost in there.'
But it was just a tramp,
Seeking shelter from the storm,
Just shivering in the damp.

When the king beheld the tramp
He said, 'Oh, sorry sight!
Ungrateful kids have caused all this,
I'll bet my crown I'm right.'

King Lear stumbled round and round;
It seemed that he were blind.
It made Earl Kent start thinking
That the king had lost his mind.

And in truth it must be said,
Though it's extremely sad,
Because of all this heartache
King Lear had gone quite mad.

At dawn the storm abated
And shortly passed right over.
Then Earl Kent transferred the king
To the castle keep at Dover.

His friends were at the castle,
That's why he took him there.
The Earl set off for France and left
King Lear in their care.

He went to fair Cordelia,
To that kind-hearted maid.
He knew that when she heard the news
She'd send the king some aid.

So hastening to the court of France
He told them everything:
The sisters' awful deeds and their
Mistreatment of the king.

He spoke with eloquence and style
In such a moving way,
Cordelia cried out loudly,
'Oh, I must set out today.'

Then to the King of France she said,
With tears in her eyes,
'My dear husband, I must go
Before my father dies.

'I must hurry to his side
Now he is all alone,
And help him to recover
His place upon the throne.'

And so the King of France agreed
An army was approved,
Cordelia sallied forth to get
Her sisters both removed.

In a convoy of great ships
They made the crossing over;
She and her army landed on
The beach quite close to Dover.

Once they were safe on shore her men
Were horrified to find
King Lear just wandering on his own –
He'd clearly lost his mind.

He had escaped his carers,
He looked just like a tramp,
But they identified him
And took him back to camp.

There he met Cordelia,
His erstwhile favourite child.
He gazed at her with piteous looks
Affectionate and wild.

He hugged her, overcome with love,
He kissed his daughter's hand,
And then his eyes glazed over –
He seemed not to understand.

Cordelia hoped in time
She might cure or ease his pain.
She vowed she would do anything
To see him well again.

Meanwhile what of the sisters?
What's been happening in their life?
Well, each of them had grown into
A most unfaithful wife.

It seems that they'd both fallen for
Exactly the same bloke,
And owing to this common love
They hardly ever spoke.

This chap, Edmund of Gloucester,
Had been given a new brief:
To lead the English army
As their commander in chief.

But then when Regan's husband died
She said with no delay,
'I'm going to wed dear Edmund,
We intend to fix the day.'

Goneril was really mad,
Extremely jealous too;
And then, inflamed by malice,
She decided what to do –

She would kill her rival sister.
So on a fateful day
She slipped her sister poison –
And poor Regan passed away.

Goneril was imprisoned
Though she denied all guilt and lied,
But seeing that there was no hope
She stabbed herself and died.

So Edmund faced the army
That had come across from France;
It was a bloody battle
Fought with sword and mace and lance.

Victory went to Edmund,
His great army won the day.
So 'What of poor Cordelia?'
I'm sure I hear you say.

Well, she was taken prisoner
And locked away in jail
Where she was almost starved to death,
Grew weak and very pale.

Then she was executed,
Life really is unfair
For she had given love to all,
A trait that's very rare.

They brought Cordelia's body
And they showed it to King Lear,
He wrapped his arms around her,
He held her very near.

'My poor child, don't die,' he cried
But he cried out in vain,
He thought he saw her breathing,
He gasped, 'She lives again.

'I think her lips were moving
For they quivered just a touch.'
Poor Lear got so excited
That the strain became too much.

He died as he held his daughter,
The child who'd been so dear,
A tragic thing to happen,
There's no happy ending here.

And so that leaves the Earl of Kent,
I wish that we could tell
He at least survived – but no,
He was to die as well.

For after King Lear's tragic death,
This servant – good and brave
Pronounced that he would follow
His master to the grave.

So there it is – a sorry tale
Where everybody dies,
A story of ingratitude,
Greed, treachery and lies.

Though Bottom looked a silly git
It was a truly perfect fit

A MIDSUMMER NIGHT'S DREAM

Now maybe you already know
In Athens many years ago,
Dads chose whom their daughters wed
And daughters did what Daddy said.

For in those distant days of yore
Athens had an awful law,
If Daddy said, 'You'll wed this guy.'
And she replied, 'I'd rather die...'

The father taking a deep breath,
Could have his daughter put to death,
So if girls wanted to grow old
They always did as they were told.

Of course most fathers loved their daughter
And could not contemplate such slaughter,
The law was very seldom used
And lovelorn girls were just excused.

But then one day a lovely girl
Fell in love, her heart awhirl,
But her Dad, Egeus, said,
'You marry him, I'll see you dead.'

Hermia, the daughter, was most sad,
She cried, 'I love Lysander, Dad.'
Egeus saw her love was true
But said, 'I've found the man for you.

'Demetrius is the one you'll wed.'
She said, 'I'd rather I were dead.'
Egeus answered this rebuke,
'I'm taking you to see the Duke.'

The Duke would tell them what to do,
His word was law, as she well knew,
She feared what now might be in store
If he applied the rule of law.

The Duke was great and fair and kind
And of a decent turn of mind,
His judgements fair on all he saw,
Right to the letter of the law.

Hermia looked into his face
And this is how she made her case –
She said, 'Demetrius is fine
But I don't want him to be mine.

'He once loved Helena, my best friend
And vowed his love would never end,
He now says he's set Helena free
And claims that he's in love with me.

'Although he says he's had his fill
My friend declares she loves him still,
She can't help her strong attraction,
She still loves him to distraction.'

Although the Duke wished to be fair
And pitied Hermia pleading there,
He said, 'Agree ere it's too late,
You must obey the laws of state.

'Marry Demetrius,' he said,
'Or otherwise you'll end up dead.
In four days time come back to me
And tell me then that you agree.'

Poor Hermia began to cry –
She really didn't want to die –
The Duke dismissed her with a plea,
'Come on,' he said. 'Do it for me.'

But Hermia had stubborn ways
And though she only had four days
To wed Demetrius or die
She stayed loyal to her guy.

When Lysander heard her fate
He said, 'Don't get in such a state,
I know exactly what to do,
I know a way to rescue you.

'My old aunt lives some way from here
And there you can be free of fear.
Only in Athens can you die;
Elsewhere this law does not apply.'

Lysander then went on to say,
'When it's dark, we'll steal away.
Tonight creep quietly from your house –
You must be quiet as a mouse.

'Then meet me in the nearby wood.
Is that all clearly understood?
Once we meet we must not tarry,
Then at my aunt's, we two can marry.'

They agreed and then they parted;
She no longer felt downhearted.
She sought out Helena that night
And told the young girl of her plight.

Helena was her friend you see,
She told her, 'We intend to flee,
And then the two of us will wed.'
'Well, good for you,' Helena said.

Now Helena had private views
About Hermia's breaking news.
Was she jealous or was she mean?
To tell the truth it's hard to glean.

For she set off and quickly ran
To tell Demetrius of the plan.
Her love for him drove her insane –
By doing this – what could she gain?

He'd follow Hermia, this she knew –
It's what his love would make him do.
Her own love, which she could not quell,
Would make her follow him as well.

The wood wherein they planned to meet
Was trodden by the tiny feet
Of little people that we call
The fairies – they are very small.

Oberon was the fairy king –
He was in charge of everything.
All the fairies understood
He was the big boss of the wood.

At one time Oberon could be seen
With fair Titania, his queen,
Joining in the fairy fun –
But now it seemed that they had none.

For every time they met at night
Within the wood by soft moon-light,
It wouldn't take them very long
Before they uttered something wrong.

They'd argue then like little devils
And destroy the midnight revels;
The fairies all would run and hide
Until the quarrel might subside.

The reason for this lack of joy
Was just a little orphaned boy.
His Mum had been Titania's friend
But giving birth had been her end.

Once she'd been taken in the hearse
The queen had fetched him from his nurse,
'I'll be your Mummy, son,' she said,
'Now that your proper Mum is dead.'

And now the boy was of the age
To make a really first class page,
And so the king was very keen
To get the young lad from the queen.

But she would not give up the boy
Though Oberon tried every ploy,
And this explains why every night
The king and queen would have a fight.

Then one night the king was walking
With his court and idly talking
When he met Titania's train
Along a shady, woodland lane.

This evening was the very night
The lovers planned their desperate flight.
They were meeting in the wood
In which the king and queen now stood.

'Fancy meeting,' said the king,
'What a most unfortunate thing!
But as you're here I'll ask again
And make my wishes very plain.

'Give me the little orphan boy.'
The queen said, 'He is not a toy.'
The king then flew into a rage,
'I simply want him for my page.'

The queen let out an angry cry:
'Your fairy kingdom couldn't buy
The boy – no matter what you say.'
And then Titania went her way.

'Go!' the king said. 'This you'll rue,
For I will be revenged on you
Before the morning clock has struck.'
And then he called his servant, Puck.

Now Puck was shrewd and keen and smart,
He made having fun an art.
'Go, Puck,' said Oberon with glee,
'And bring that purple flower to me.

'We'll make some juice and then we'll creep
Up to the queen while she's asleep.
Then place it on her eyelids so,
Softly, then she will not know.

'When she wakes whom first she sees
Will bring a tremor to her knees,
And she will swear to heaven above
That she is passionately in love.'

Puck loved this mischief and this fun
And went off at a frantic run.
He said, 'I'll go and get the flower
And I'll be back within the hour.'

The king awaited Puck's return.
Then through the trees he did discern
Demetrius – and Helena too,
And she was calling, 'I love you'.

Demetrius was saying, 'Go!'
He really didn't want to know.
He gave the girl a little shove –
She said, 'What happened to your love?'

Demetrius said, 'You let me be,
Clear off and do not hassle me.'
She found this very hard to swallow
And so resolved that she would follow.

Now Oberon, the fairy king,
Invisible, heard everything;
And as he watched events unfurl
He felt compassion for the girl.

Now he knew he had the power,
Once he had the magic flower,
To make old Cupid send a dart
Right to Demetrius' heart.

When Puck returned, he said, 'Forsooth,
Yonder walks an uncouth youth,
And a girl whose heart does burn
With love the youth does not return.

'When you find this man asleep
I want you quietly to creep
And stop him waking in surprise,
Then drop the juice onto his eyes.

'Ensure the lady is close by
So she's the first he does espy.
Go now, my Puck, and do your worst,
But make quite sure he sees *her* first.'

Then King Oberon, having kept
Some juice, went where Titania slept.
He placed it on her eyes and said,
'You'll love the first you see.' – then fled.

Meanwhile, as quietly as she could
Hermia left home for the wood.
She made her way with every care
And found Lysander waiting there.

Though weary, Hermia did her best
Until she sighed, 'I must have rest.'
So having found a mossy mound
They both lay down upon the ground.

'Sleep till morn,' Lysander said.
'This mossy ground shall be your bed.'
Soon they were both soundly sleeping;
Then it was that Puck came creeping.

When he spotted them asleep
He took a very careful peep,
Then to himself he said, 'In truth,
This is the girl and this the youth.'

The king had meant the juice to be
For young Demetrius, you see,
But Puck should not take all the blame
Because most youths look just the same.

Puck had made a small mistake –
Easily done, for goodness' sake.
He ran off, having got it wrong,
Just as Helena came along.

Demetrius had run ahead –
He'd left her all alone and fled,
But now she saw Lysander here
She thought there's nothing more to fear.

'Lysander – oh, for mercy's sake,
If you're alive, then please awake.'
She had no thought of causing harm,
She didn't know about the charm.

Lysander rubbed his tired eyes,
On hearing Helena's close cries;
His eyes met hers and in a tick
The juice had worked its artful trick.

He said, 'Oh Helena, my dove,
It's you alone I truly love.'
Helena knew he was engaged
So rightly she felt most enraged.

She said, 'Why do you speak this way,
Whatever would your Hermia say?
Please explain at once this mystery.'
He responded, 'Hermia's history.

'We're not an item anymore –
In fact she's really quite a bore.'
Helena said, 'Love's not a game,
All you men are made the same.'

She spoke with vigour and with candour:
'I thought more of you, Lysander.'
Then, having had her tearful say,
She turned around and ran away.

Lysander followed quickly too
To show her that his love was true;
He left poor Hermia fast asleep –
Despite the noise she made no peep.

When Hermia woke all on her own
She was alarmed to be alone.
Wherever could Lysander be?
Whatever could have made him flee?

Why had he gone without a word?
What in the world could have occurred?
She set out then, fast as she could,
To search for him throughout the wood.

Meanwhile Demetrius searched too,
He searched the dense wood through and through,
His love for Hermia spurred him on,
Where in the world could she have gone?

Lost and wondering what to do
He grew sleepy – and slept too.
Then through the wood by great good luck
Came Oberon and his servant Puck.

The king had now found out from Puck
How his smart plan had come unstuck,
How he'd applied the love charm to
The wrong man – all of this you knew.

The king would have his way and whim –
He said, 'We must put some on *him* –
The one you put it on was wrong
For I meant this one all along.'

So as Demetrius lay there
The king poured juice on him with care;
He poured it onto each eyelid
Then they both left the scene and hid.

Just at the moment they withdrew
Sleepy Demetrius came to,
Then Helena came on the scene
And stood right where the sprites had been.

So as Demetrius awoke
He saw fair Helena and spoke
Of love and things that would disarm,
For he was influenced by the charm.

Helena thought, 'How can this be?'
But then she was surprised to see
Lysander coming into view
With tearful Hermia following too.

And now Lysander spoke of love:
He said he loved her way above
All other girl's he'd ever known,
Helena was completely thrown.

For as he cried out, 'I love you.'
Demetrius said, 'And I do too.'
Helena said, 'Why joke this way?
It is the most unkind display.'

Poor Hermia was most astonished.
'What's going on?' the girl admonished.
'Now Helena is this all true:
Though they loved me, they now love you?'

'It does seem so,' Helena said,
'They seem to love me now instead.'
Then words between the girls got terse
And things just went from bad to worse.

For the two youths withdrew from sight
Determined now to have a fight,
Both swearing to the heavens above
That they would die for Helena's love.

Puck and Oberon saw them go,
The king said, 'What a so and so!
Puck, we must try and put things right –
We've really got to stop this fight.

'So overhang the wood with fog,
Go now and make the thickest smog,
And in your cunning, devious way
Lead these two warring lads astray.

'Imitate their cries,' he said.
'Make them follow where they're led,
If each hears what he thinks to be
His rival's voice, he'll run to see.

'Lead them around the wood until
They're tired out and feel quite ill;
Then wait until they fall asleep,
And when their sleep is very deep,

'Then creep up to their makeshift bower
And drop the juice of this new flower
Onto Lysander's closed eyelids
And that should sort out all these kids.

'For when he wakes he'll not recall
The happenings of this night at all;
He'll love Hermia as before
And not poor Helena anymore.

'And then I think we will discern
That their old passion will return,
It will rekindle the old fire,
Each girl will have whom they desire.

'Do it now, Puck, and do it well,
Do it exactly as I tell,
Then when they wake it all will seem
That what has passed was but a dream.'

When Puck had done this he then crept
To where fair Queen Titania slept.
But someone else just caught his eye...
It was a man asleep close by.

His name was Bottom, sad to say,
And he'd completely lost his way,
And then as Puck looked at the man
He hatched a really fiendish plan.

'*He* shall be her love,' he said.
And then he took an ass's head,
And placed it on the man's and sighed,
'It's perfect – not too tall or wide.'

Though Bottom looked a silly git
It was a truly perfect fit,
And though Puck had not made a sound
Poor Bottom started coming round.

He woke but he was unaware
Of his transformation there.
He took a look around the scene,
And soon beheld the sleeping queen.

Then Titania woke and said
As she looked at the ass's head,
'What is this lovely sight I see?
An angel surely it must be.

'And are you also wise as well,
Now speak up boldly and please tell.'
Said Bottom from his ass's hood,
'I want to get out of this wood.'

'Don't speak of leaving,' said the queen.
The juice was making her most keen
To try and get the man to stay,
She said, 'Oh, please don't go away.

'Do not trifle now with me,
This is no common sprite you see,
If you stay here and start anew
My fairies will look after you.

'They'll wait upon your every need –
Their names are Moth and Mustardseed,
And Peaseblossom and Cobweb too –
They'll all love looking after you.'

She said to them, 'Do all you can
For my new love, this gentleman.'
And then to Bottom said, 'Come here
And let me kiss your hairy ear.'

But Bottom didn't fancy this,
He really didn't want a kiss,
So he ignored her fervent plea
And said, 'Fairies, attend to me.'

He told the fairies what to do –
'Scratch my head now one of you.'
He thought up other silly pranks
And gave no single word of thanks.

When he had asked all he desired
He told the queen, 'I'm feeling tired.'
She said, 'Recline upon my lap,
And have yourself a little nap.'

She wrapped her arms around his head,
'Sleep softly now, my love,' she said,
He slept as she sang him a song,
The king at this point came along.

'What's this?' says he. 'Unfaithful lass,
Why are you cuddling with an ass?'
The queen went red and very coy,
The king said, 'I still want that boy.'

The queen looked guiltily at him –
How could she now refuse his whim?
So it does not take much to guess
That very quickly she said, 'Yes.'

She was embarrassed to be found
With loving arms wrapped all around
An ass! So what then could she do?
She said, 'I'll give the boy to you.'

Now that the king had got his way –
Unfairly, some of you might say –
He had a mind to call a truce
So took out some of the new juice.

He threw it in Titania's eyes
And so destroyed her loving sighs.
She said, 'I have been very crass,
How could I love that ugly ass?

'I must have been a bit insane –
Oh please let us be friends again.'
She showed regret and much remorse
So Oberon said, 'Yes, of course.'

Then he removed the ass's head.
'We'll let this fool sleep on,' he said.
They crept away without a word,
So softly that they went unheard.

The king said to the queen, 'Now wait,
And I will bring you up to date.'
He told her what had passed that night,
About the lovers and their plight.

And then he took her where they were
Sleeping sound beneath a fir;
Puck in his cleverness had got
All four lovers to one spot.

Hermia woke up first and thought
Lysander's love had fallen short;
Then he awoke and saw her there
And spoke to her with loving care.

As they talked about that night
They saw that things were now all right.
'We're still in love – so it does seem
That everything was just a dream.'

And then Demetrius awoke,
Quite clearly a besotted bloke,
As Helena woke up then too
He turned and said, 'I do love you.'

He was in love with her once more,
In just the way he'd been before;
The love juice made his passion burn
And made his love for her return.

Helena was pleased to hear
His words which sounded so sincere,
So as our tale now all but ends
The four of them were once more friends.

But then with horror and surprise
In disbelief they rubbed their eyes –
Hermia's father had appeared;
It was the thing that she most feared.

He angrily had searched the wood,
But when Egeus understood
That Demetrius would not wed
His daughter, he then turned and said,

'What fickle things the fates have sent!
I will reluctantly consent
For you to be Lysander's wife,
So fear no longer for your life.

'You now can marry,' he then said.
'In fact all four of you can wed.'
So all things ended very well
And there is nothing more to tell.

Except to say this tale may seem
As if it was some kind of dream,
And you may very well be right;
A dream – on a midsummer's night.